THE HUMAN ANIMAL

The Mystery of Man's Behavior

THE
HUMAN
ANIMAL

The Mystery of Man's Behavior

by HANS HASS

G. P. Putnam's Sons

New York

Translated from the German
by J. Maxwell Brownjohn

Originally published under the title *Wir Menschen:*
Das Geheimnis unseres Verhaltens. Copyright © 1968
by Verlag Fritz Molden.

PRINTED IN THE UNITED STATES OF AMERICA

Only the acme of man is man.

PARACELSUS

The animal is taught by its organs; man teaches his and controls them.

GOETHE

I contend that the uniqueness of man cannot be seen in all its imposing grandeur unless it is set off against the background of those ancient historical characteristics which man still shares with the higher forms of animal life today.

KONRAD LORENZ

Contents

Point of Departure   9

PART ONE   *Animal Behavior*

1. Animal and Human Behavior   17
2. Innate Behavior Patterns   22
3. Innate Recognition   30
4. Instinct and Mood   41
5. Acquired Behavior   51
6. And What of Man?   66

PART TWO   *Human Behavior*

7. A Voyage of Self-Exploration   79
8. Man and Curiosity   87
9. Artificial Organs   100
10. The Barometer of the Soul   110
11. The Friendship Signal   120
12. Man and Order   132
13. Gestures   142
14. Man and Multicellular Organism   152
15. Imprinting and Freedom   162
16. Man and Society   175

8 · Contents

17. Man and Imagination   186
18. The Quest for Happiness   199

Epilogue   215

Appendices

Key to Sources   223
Bibliography   229
Index   241

Illustration sections appear after pages 96 and 160.

Point of Departure

WHAT makes man "different"? We now know that he evolved from the animal kingdom, yet animal and human being are separated by a wide gulf. In a recently published book, the British zoologist Desmond Morris portrayed man as a "naked ape" with an exceptionally well-developed penis. His intention was wholly serious. No sooner do we tackle the question "What are we?" than we become bogged down in the welter of opinions that have already been expressed on this subject. Almost every one of the countless religious, philosophical, sociological, psychological, anthropological, and zoological views of the nature of man appears to contain a germ of truth, yet an unbridgeable chasm continues to separate us from our past. This book is an attempt to view man's peculiarity as part of the overall development of the life process. It investigates the problem of what parts of our behavior can be accounted for by our ancestry and may thus be construed as a further development of animal behavior. Beyond that, it explores three additional questions. What is it that truly lies at the root of our great "differentness"? How did we attain our present position of superiority? And, finally, how did the life process, in the structural type known as man, gain such complete supremacy over all hitherto existing specimens in the animal and vegetable kingdoms?

9

The great difficulty that must be overcome in any study of man is that we, the observers, are men ourselves; that our brain, being an instrument of study, is itself an object of study. We are surrounded by human beings all our lives, with the result that we take society and all that it imprints upon us for granted. It is all but impossible for us to speculate about that which seems so natural, view it from a different and unbiased angle, climb out of our own bodies—*become strangers to ourselves.*

The idea of studying man from an extraneous vantage point —in other words, as something completely foreign and novel— occurred to me years ago during my research work in tropical waters. Hundreds of times we went over the side with our diving equipment and drifted down—into the unknown. Vague outlines emerged from the twilit depths and took shape, and we found ourselves constantly confronted by alien realms of existence. Observing the numerous corals, sponges, fish, and crustaceans, we endeavored to grasp why, in the course of evolution, they had deveoped this or that particular physical shape, this or that mode of behavior. A visitor from another world, approaching our planet in an invisible spaceship, would presumably find himself in a similar position. He too would begin by observing vague outlines, then look down on a flurry of alien life in which the creature known as man would doubtless hold special interest for him. He would know nothing of our history, nothing of our thought processes. All he would see of us initially would be moving bodies, and he would very probably ask himself how such creatures had attained such a considerable degree of development.

To the biologist, there is no very great or fundamental difference between man and beast. The laws which once governed the life and physical appearance of marine organisms continued to govern the life and physical appearance of plants and animals when these had conquered dry land. The same laws governed the beginnings of human evolution, which subsequently deviated so far from "nature" that we find it hard to discern or acknowledge the connection today. Was it not possible, I wondered, to study these most remarkable of all living creatures— oursleves—with the same objectivity that we reserve for, say, the study of marine life?

The camera, I thought, might be able to help me here. From elevated observation posts, I tried to film city dwellers just as I had filmed fish thronging the coral reefs, varying the camera speed so that all movement appeared many times more rapid when the film was projected. The results were promising. These sequences transformed scenes of familiar activity into something akin to an ant heap. The individuality of different persons largely vanished, and transcendent factors became visible. Events at an intersection displayed a rhythmically pulsating pattern. The gestures of people buying from sidewalk stalls or engaged in conversation took on different aspects. With one farmer and his wife, whom I filmed from above while they were haymaking, the pattern of their organized cooperation became clearly apparent. Incidents which at normal speed appeared mundane and banal became exciting and novel when accelerated. Obviously, the brain was not attuned to such timing.

I reran many sequences a dozen times or more and found that each viewing disclosed something new. Patterns emerged which would normally have passed unnoticed; first, because the mind is habituated to such procedures and automatically fits them into a thought pattern, and second, because they occur too slowly to be noticed in normal observation.

With a number of close-ups I altered the timing in the other direction. I "stretched" these telephoto sequences or filmed them in slow motion, and a similar alienation effect came into play. Normal judgments lost their meaning so far as these films were concerned. A common element, only partly disguised by individual differences, emerged. The screen no longer showed a mere face but an undulating plain upon which movements ran their course. These movements—smiling or frowning, for example—still elicited the reactions normally produced by recognition of their significance, but subjective reactions also receded. There was less appeal to the emotions and more freedom for the eye to follow each facial movement critically and leisurely. I noticed, however, that only films shot unobserved produced this effect.

Having used a photographic subterfuge to study various human behavioral patterns, I wondered if reality might not have been so distorted by changes of speed that I was drawing false conclusions. This doubt was quickly dispelled. As every scientist knows, speed is never absolute. More than a century ago, the zoologist Karl Ernst von Baer pointed out that the human time sense is relative and differs from that of many animals. A living creature's notion of time derives from the number of impressions which its central nervous system can process in a given unit of time. Insects, for example, react considerably faster than man, as the sight of a darting fly clearly demonstrates. It is obvious that they can process impressions faster than we can, hence the passage of time must seem relatively slower to them. To them, the human being must appear to move in slow motion. Other creatures react more slowly—*e.g.*, snails, to which the human being must appear an extremely fast-moving creature. Thus, by artificially distorting the passage of time, I was abandoning the subjective, human mode of observation, not falsifying reality in any way.

But there was another problem. Regular movements seemed even more regular in greatly accelerated sequences than they really were. An example of this was a film I had made of a ball in Vienna, projected at ten times the actual speed. The young men and women dancing the polonaise were far from faultless; indeed several of them broke ranks. But in the accelerated film, by contrast, the couples were invested with great precision by the marionettelike rapidity with which they rotated and formed lines. Here, the brain was obviously ironing out irregularities. And yet, an analogous falsification occurs in our normal perception of material objects. Only because our brains emphasize common and regular features are we in a position to make a swift and effective assessment of the world and classify its contents. The human capacity for Gestalt perception, seeing things as a whole and not as separate parts, made its appearance here, as it does in general.

Armed with this new technique, I proceeded to make films in all five continents in association with Dr. Irenaeus Eibl-Eibesfeldt (of the Max Planck Institute of Behavioral Physiology, Seewiesen), and studying these films helped us evolve many new methods of observation.

In the first part of this book I premise a summary of those features of animal behavior with which anyone who wishes to

undertake a scientific study of human behavior must be acquainted. The reader versed in biology will find little that is
new to him. The reader less conversant with science—and it is
to him that I should like to appeal in particular—is intended to
regard this section as a bridge to biological thinking.

The second part sets forth the results of our investigations,
together with a number of more general observations on how
the various facets of human life (political organization, economics, education, art, religion, entertainment, etc.) appear when
viewed from the evolutionary standpoint. The principle of artificial organs, here expounded for the first time, runs counter to
various currently popular basic tenets and buttresses my demand
for a completely new and different classification of man within
the zoological system. Because it repeatedly emerges in the course
of discussion that misapprehensions arise from wrongly understood words, I have made a special effort to clarify all the expressions employed here. I have attempted to avoid technical
terms which are not universally familiar.

I should like to take this opportunity of expressing my thanks
to my friend Dr. Irenaeus Eibl-Eibesfeldt, whose comprehen-
sive knowledge of research into animal behavior (see source nos.
33 and 34 in the Bibliography) paved the way for the ethological
aspect of our endeavors. Many of the ideas advanced in this book
matured in the course of discussions which took place between
us during joint filming expeditions all over the world.

PART I

Animal Behavior

I

Animal and Human Behavior

C AN we learn much about our own behavior from studying that of animals? Can the study of a beetle or a rat tell us something about man's basic drives? Can we solve problems of psychology or sociology by devoting our attention to the giraffe, dancing fly, and segmented worm?

Human actions—we tell ourselves—are the products of conscious mental acts and are thus essentially different from those of animals. It is vaguely humiliating even to consider the idea of comparison. We human beings are (as far as we can ascertain) the only creatures to possess an awareness of self, the only creatures endowed with reason. We can consciously direct our actions with an eye to the future. We have produced immensely complex codes of religious, moral, and aesthetic behavior. We have, by using our ability to think, created complex political and economic organizations which have no comparable counterparts in the animal kingdom. We have many truly grandiose cultural and technological advances. What can the lowly worm teach us which might add to our self-knowledge? The bee, the whale, the lion—these are living creatures like ourselves and to that extent related to us. But when it comes to assessing ourselves and to understanding a creature as obviously superior and fundamentally different as man, surely they can be of little

use or, at best, can enable us to draw nothing more than unimportant and superficial parallels.

On the other hand, the theory of evolution is largely accepted. Indeed, actually it is no longer a theory and has become the cornerstone of the biological edifice. All that still
remains open is the question as to what forces and causes this
remarkable development—evolution—should be attributed.

There are three conflicting schools of thought here. The vitalists believe in an extrasensory force which guides organisms
toward a higher state of perfection. The Lamarckians believe
in the heritability of acquired characteristics—a theory which
would greatly facilitate our understanding of evolution but has
yet to be proven, and, indeed, has largely been discredited. Finally, most present-day biologists espouse the mutation theory,
according to which the upward evolution of organisms has been
effected by random inherited changes. The role of the natural-
selection process to which Darwin drew attention is by no means
confined to the last-named theory. Rather, it has been a decisive factor in any speculation on the emergence of new forms.
However new animals or plants may have come into being,
they must in every case have had to contend with different and
often vicissitudinous living conditions. As a result, they managed to assert themselves only when they equaled or surpassed
their rivals' capacity for survival.

In view of the evidence assembled during the last 100 years,
there can be no serious doubt that all higher animals and
plants are descended from unicellular organisms. We can now
state, with a confidence verging on certainty, that insects and
spiders are descended from marine arthropods; that existing
terrestrial vertebrates evolved from fish; that reptiles are descended from amphibians; that from reptiles there evolved
birds on the one hand and mammals on the other; and that
man is descended from two now-extinct branches of the large
ape family. We are thus related not only to apes but also to
lizards, batrachians, fish, unicellular organisms—yes, even to
plants.

The Christian religion no longer adopts a hostile attitude
toward the theory of evolution. On the Roman Catholic side,
the Pope himself commented on the problem in 1950, in the

encyclical *Humani generis.* The Catholic Church now holds that primeval man, being descended from the ape family, acquired his immortal soul by divine afflatus in the Early Pleistocene period, or about 800,000 years ago. According to this doctrine, therefore, God made use of an existing animal body and transformed it into man by an act of creation.

We have long grown accustomed to some of the consequences which stem from our kinship with animals. For instance, few people find it disturbing that numerous drugs are developed and tested by means of experiments on animals. Since many of the hormones at work inside us are the same as those in the more closely related animals, we extract them from their glands and inject them, as required, into man. Examples are the thyroid hormone, insulin, and the male sex hormone. Our knowledge of the function of human muscles and human nerve cells is based on experiments conducted principally with frogs, fish, and rodents. And our very advanced knowledge of human heredity and of the complex structure of human hereditary factors was gained predominantly from experiments with the pea (in other words, a plant), the porpoise, and the fruit fly *Drosophila.* None of this would be possible were it not for the existence of a genuine relationship.

Turning to the subject of human behavior—that is to say, the reasons why we select this or that particular way of life, what motives govern our various actions, and the way we react to given situations—we find that this complex of problems still falls within the competency of sciences which pay little or no heed to the fact of our evolution. The main questions explored by philosophy, psychology, sociology, and other sciences concerned with human behavior are rooted in conceptual systems which developed in an age when man's descent from the animal kingdom was still unknown. To them, man is not only a focus of observation but the starting point of almost every discussion. Now that our origins are no longer in doubt, however, it is only logical that man's behavior should be seen against the background of our animal descent—that we should proceed from the modest beginnings of a long chain rather than from its final link. Only by asking what in our behavior still links us with our animal past can we ascertain the nature of our peculiarity —our differentness.

Human beings have shown themselves extremely skillful at mastering their environment, and technological progress has brought us a breathtaking accretion of power. No such enormous strides are demonstrable in the field of intraspecific behavior, or human coexistence. As always, humanity's progress is characterized by crime and war. As always, the individual remains subject to highly mysterious whims and moods which all too often prompt him to irrational conduct. As always, whole communities and races are gripped by the most destructive passions. Here man is confronted by peculiarities of temperament which are demonstrably rooted, not in his intellect, but in far deeper "layers" of his nature. Human nature being possibly—or even probably—the remains of an ancient heritage and explicable only by reference to our descent, what could be more logical than to place this heritage, this ancestry, in the forefront of our research—indeed, to make it our point of departure? Is this not the best way of coping with just these deeper layers in our nature, with just this mysterious nature which dwells within us?

Konrad Lorenz, the founder of modern behavioral research (ethology), pointed out years ago that knowledge obtained from the study of animal behavior ought to be applied to the better understanding of human behavior. He described this as "the most important practical task" confronting this branch of research and has himself been responsible for numerous initiatives in this direction. His words found little favor with students of the human mind, however, and no reorientation toward this totally different point of departure—which in practice begins with the smallest of all primitive living creatures—has yet been undertaken.

American environmentalists, in particular, take the view that practically all human behavior is acquired, and that man can therefore be molded at will by upbringing and education. Animal behavior is likewise attributed almost entirely to learning processes. The European schools of behavioral research, particularly those of Lorenz and the Dutch zoologist Tinbergen, have arrived at quite different conclusions. Exhaustive experiments have shown that many elements in the behavior of animals, even of the most closely related higher mammals, are fixed by heredity. The results of this research suggest that human behavior is probably more predetermined than we realize.

The following chapters are intended to present the major results of behavioral research in as easily digestible a form as possible. The aim is to show what basic biological conditions gave rise to the individual phenomena and effects of animal behavior, from which human behavior evolved.

2

Innate Behavior Patterns

ET us begin with a general statement such as the visitor from another planet would make if he were interested in the nature of life on our own. Every living creature, whether we call it plant or animal, is characterized by a very particular physical shape which is always transmitted by the individual to its descendants. There is no recorded instance of a grasshopper begetting a mouse, nor has a sycamore seed ever produced a violet. This sounds quite obvious, and it seems still more obvious that no violet will spring from the seed of a grasshopper, nor a mouse from that of a sycamore tree.

However, the position is not quite as straightforward as it appears. Animals and plants always spring from a single cell, and these germ cells possess the same essential structure. In many cases it is far from easy to tell at first glance, even under the microscope, whether a particular germ cell will develop into a plant or an animal.

The germ cell divides, and the resultant new cells separate—which is how unicellular organisms multiply. Alternatively, division proceeds as before, but the cells adhere to one another and differentiate themselves in various ways by forming tissue and organs—which is the origin of large and very dissimilar bodies such as those we call violet or earthworm, sycamore or mouse. These multicellular organisms consist of millions—indeed, billions—of individual cells, all of which issued from single cells of fundamentally the same type.

Somewhere in the germ cells, therefore, reside very dissimilar controlling "formulas" which impose a quite specific mode of behavior upon the emergent daughter cells—though in this instance we speak not of behavior, which it is in the strictest sense, but development. The questions of what these developmental formulas actually look like, where they are located, and how they operate have largely been solved. Thanks to one of the present century's major feats of biological research, we know that these special formulas are carried by the chromosomes which reside in the cell nuclei. As we now know, these consist of minute threads arranged like a spiral staircase, on which, as in a pearl necklace, are distributed various groups of atoms (radicals). These may be likened to letters which spell out the commands of heredity. Their sequence determines how individual cells behave during development; in other words, whether they become a mouse or a sycamore.

We apply the word "behavior" in its true sense to something else, namely, the movement of an entire organism in space. Such behavior is seen principally in animals, but sometimes it occurs in plants as well, though with plants movements are so slow that they can be seen with clarity only in accelerated films. For instance, many flowers open during the day and close when evening comes. Many leaves turn to face the light. The tendrils of climbing plants describe spiral movements until they find a purchase and anchor themselves. The leaves of some carnivorous plants snap shut, in trap fashion. The best-known reactive movements are those of the mimosa, which can be clearly seen with the naked eye. All these active movements are caused by growth processes or by fluctuations in sap pressure within the cells (turgor). There is no doubt that the regulation of such movements in the plants in question is as much determined by heredity as is the conformation of their various organs.

Many behavior patterns are likewise anchored in heredity in the case of animals. The hereditary formula builds up those structures which effect control of such movements. A duckling, for instance, has a whole repertory of actions available and ready for use as soon as it leaves the egg. It can already walk and swim excellently, it already dabbles in mud with its beak and cleans its plumage in a characteristic manner. Each of these motor sequences entails hundreds—indeed, thousands—of separate but coordinated commands which must travel by way of various nerves to the numerous muscles which carry out the movements. Viewed as a whole, the duckling's walk or preening movements appear extremely simple. However, the true structural complexity of even such simple actions can be gauged by observing a child as it laboriously learns the noninnate motor sequence involved in eating with a spoon. Protracted experimentation is required before the child manages to coordinate the muscular movements of hand and arm in such a way that the spoon picks up food and conveys it neatly to the mouth. Were it possible to draw a circuit diagram of what underlies this procedure in the central nervous system, we should no doubt be dumbfounded by its intricacy.

The butterfly is innately endowed with the far more difficult art of flying. It is capable of taking the air as soon after it emerges from the chrysalis as its wings have hardened. The young human has an innate ability to find its mother's breast and suck. The tiny little slipper animalcule, which lives in drops of water, is innately capable of propelling itself forward with strokes from more than a thousand cilia, or minute hair-like appendages, and of retreating when it meets an obstacle. When these unicellular organisms divide, the new individuals thus formed can swim quite normally—their cilia strokes are already coordinated properly. Each of these cases poses the same question: Where are the formulas for these innate movements located, and from what part of the body are they controlled?

Little is known about this in the case of unicellular organisms. In that of multicellular creatures we know that the nerve cells are the carriers of these controlling formulas. But we do not know what these structures look like. They may depend on a "wiring" of individual cells similar to that in an electrical circuit, or they may be molecular differentiations resembling the developmental formulas in chromosomes. At all events, they are functional units which may fairly be compared with organs. Like organs, they have a very definite function to fulfill within the body's work-sharing system.

These structures, which thus prescribe a quite distinct coordination of muscular movements, mature in exactly the same way as organs. In other words, they become complete and ready to function on a particular day. This can be deduced from the fact that they sometimes fail to reach maturity at the same time as the organs whose movements they control. The cricket, for example, does not begin its characteristic chirping until some days after the formation of its "musical instruments" because it obviously lacks the requisite "score." Grasshopper larvae, by contrast, describe typical "music-making" motions with their hind legs at an early stage but fail to produce any sound because in this case their "instruments" are not yet fully developed. It has even been possible to prove, in the case of worms, crickets, bees, and fish, that formulas for the control of movement conform to the Mendelian laws of heredity. If parents which differ in their innate movements—the student of behavior calls them hereditary coordinations—are crossed, all their offspring display either the behavior of one parent or mixed behavior, whereas in the second generation the specific motor characteristics of both grandparents recur.

Many biologists refer to such nerve structures as mechanisms —a word easily misinterpreted by the layman. Far from being intended as a comparison with the machine, the term was selected because these structures function in a regular and predictable manner and thus conform perfectly to the laws of physics and chemistry. What, then, do these mechanisms of innate motor control actually achieve? Above all, what aspects of the behavior of various animal species are actually rooted in heredity in the form of hereditary coordinations?

Numerous students of behavior have devoted exhaustive experiments to this question.* Controversy with American psychologists was particularly instrumental in stimulating research on this subject. Its special difficulty lies in the fact that many movements which are innate or genuine hereditary coordinations in themselves cannot be performed at birth because the control structure has yet to mature. This may create the impression that a creature has acquired a particular motor pattern

* Not all authorities are mentioned by name in the text. Individual publications may be identified by referring to the source key on p. 223 and checked in the Bibliography.

by learning, whereas careful experimentation shows that its behavior is probably innate but took time to mature.

Grohmann, for example, reared doves, some normally and the rest in cages too cramped to allow them to move their wings. As soon as the normally reared birds could fly well, he released the others. It turned out that the latter could fly with equal ease. This clearly showed that flying, an extremely difficult form of locomotion, does not have to be acquired by these birds and is at their disposal complete, like their organs. Their control structure matures somewhat later, however. The American researchers Carmichael and Fromme carried out a similar experiment with tadpoles. They reared one group normally, the rest under permanent anesthesia so that they did not move and therefore could not learn. When the anesthetic was discontinued, the drugged tadpoles proved to be able to swim almost as well as the others.

It has now been demonstrated that many animal movements are rooted in the complete genetic apparatus (genome). Innate in the garden spider is the spinning of its magnificent web, in honey bees the intricate "tail dance" with which they communicate, in the collared turtledove the method of feeding its young, in the common whitethroat its twenty-five specific calls, in the rat its copulatory motions, in the duck its exceptionally complicated mating movements, and so on. Experiments in isolated rearing cannot, of course, be carried out with human beings, but corresponding indications exist even here. Eibl verified the occurrence of normal smiling in a congenitally deaf-mute child, although it could certainly not have acquired the habit. We shall deal with the problem of human facial expressions in due course.

The aptness of the term "mechanism" for these innate structures of motor control becomes apparent when we take a closer look at their performances in matching experiments. Fabré and many other students of animal behavior were struck by how little the so-called instinctive actions had to do with intelligence and how little associated they were with a sense of purpose. The ease with which they can be simulated is often deceptive.

The digger wasp, for instance, seems to display highly intelligent brood-tending behavior. Having dug a nest, it flies off in search of a caterpillar, overpowers and kills it, drags it into the nest, and lays eggs on it. The emerging young are thereby provided with the nourishment they need and find protection in the nest, which the wasp seals. Interrupt the sequence of part-actions, however, and it soon becomes clear that no form of intelligence is at work here. Returning to its hole with the caterpillar, the wasp first deposits it in the entrance and inspects the interior, then reappears at the entrance, head foremost, and drags its quarry inside. If, while the wasp is inspecting its hole, the caterpillar is removed and deposited some distance away, the wasp will continue to search until it has rediscovered the caterpillar and then will drag it to the entrance again, whereupon the whole cycle—depositing, inspecting, etc.—begins all over again. Take away the caterpillar ten or twenty times, and the wasp will still deposit it at the entrance and embark on a tour of the hole, with which it is thoroughly familiar by this time. The insect continues to be guided by the same commands, in computer fashion, and evidently finds it hard to make any change in the overall sequence. Only after thirty or forty repetitions will the wasp finally drag the caterpillar into its nest without further inspection. Yet the digger wasp shows a great aptitude for learning where other procedures are concerned. While in flight, it memorizes the route which it must take on the ground when returning to the nest with its prey— a very considerable feat of learning. On the other hand, the burial of its prey is an instinctive action and, thus, strongly programmed. The wasp is almost incapable of influencing or altering this part of its behavior by learning, because it is controlled by an innate and extremely incorrigible mechanism.

Once stimulated, whole cycles of action can proceed by themselves. In the squirrel, food storing consists of the following part-actions: scraping away soil, depositing the nut, tamping it down with the muzzle, covering it over, and pressing down the soil. A squirrel reared indoors will still perform these actions in full, even in the absence of soil. It carries the nut into a corner, where it starts to dig, deposits the nut in the (non-existent) hole, rams it home with its muzzle (even though it merely rolls away in the process), covers up the imaginary hole, and presses down the nonexistent soil. And the squirrel still does all these things even when scrupulous care has been taken to ensure that it has never set eyes on a nut before or been given an opportunity to dig or conceal objects.

Such observations lead directly to another question. What is it that triggers off hereditary coordinations in the individual, and what special stimuli activate the mechanisms that control them?

Simple reflexes are known in almost all multicellular creatures. The organism responds to a very specific stimulus in a very specific way. Nip a decapitated frog's toe, and it will retract its leg. The reflex travels via the spinal cord, so the brain is not essential to this performance. Sensory nerve fibers are linked with the motor variety in such a way that a specific stimulus elicits a specific muscular movement. In human beings the pupil of the eye is controlled by a similar reflex: Dim light causes our optical aperture to expand, strong light causes contraction. It was naturally assumed that hereditary coordinations, too, are attributable to such reflexes—that they comprise a whole system of such reflexes. Here, however, the question becomes far less straightforward, and this brings us to a most significant discovery from the standpoint of behavioral research.

The physiologist von Holst carried out the following experiment: He severed an eel's head from its spinal cord—the center from which its sinuous swimming motions are controlled—and also cut all remaining (sensory) nerves leading to the spinal cord. This meant that the spinal cord could receive no more extraneous sensory messages and was completely cut off from the outside world. Von Holst had left the (motor) nerves leading to the muscles intact, so that the spinal cord could still issue commands to the muscles. The results were surprising. As soon as the eel recovered from postoperative shock, it performed well-coordinated wriggling motions, an activity which continued without interruption until the creature's death.

This discovery was extremely interesting from two points of view. In the first place it refuted the view of the Russian biologist Ivan P. Pavlov and his school that all instinctive actions are attributable to chains of reflexes. According to this theory, which was then supported by the majority of biologists, the movement of one segment of muscle should have activated the next in sequence by means of internal sensory impulses. The regularity of the eel's swimming had hitherto been construed as a chain reflex of this kind. However, von Holst's preparatory work had precluded the possibility of return messages to the spinal cord, so the segments could not influence one another. Second, and almost more important, his experiment showed that this series of movements, which was obviously controlled from one point, did not have to be activated by an external stimulus. On the contrary, the motor cells which governed the wriggling motion were spontaneously active.

Further experiments have since confirmed this crucial realization. The nerve cells which operate the hereditary coordinations are in a state of ceaseless activity and "fire off" their coordinatetd commands constantly. Normally, however, they are inhibited. Another nerve structure—another mechanism—blocks the movement and prevents nerve impulses from reaching the executive muscles except at very specific, biologically appropriate points in time. Ethologists, or students of behavior, call this inhibitory nerve structure (which no one has yet seen and whose existence can only be inferred) the innate releasing mechanism, or IRM for short. It is this mechanism which determines when the incessant stream of commands may reach the corresponding executive organs.

From this there arise the further questions: When does the IRM issue its releasing commands, and to what stimuli does it respond?

3

Innate Recognition

VERY organism is bombarded by a vast number and variety of stimuli which come flooding in from all sides, and the more acute its sensory organs are the more numerous will be the stimuli which it picks up. How, then, can an animal select from this profusion of sensory messages those which are essential to its existence and relevant to the survival of itself and its species? This is the gargantuan problem with which every animal "construction" has had to contend in the course of evolution.

The animal must, logically, perform the motions of feeding only when it has found suitable nourishment, otherwise they would be pointless and even distracting. Flight motions are expedient only when danger threatens, and danger must be recognized. The complicated series of movements associated with courtship and mating are also pointless unless the animal has found a suitable mate. The central nervous system must exercise an investigatory and selective function here. It must somehow recognize specific combinations of stimuli.

As numerous experiments have shown, IRM's (innate releasing mechanisms) are finely attuned to particular combinations of stimuli, much as a key is tailored to a lock. Just as the key opens the lock, so a particular stimulus acts on the IRM in such a way that it gives the go-ahead to the nerve impulses, and the appropriate hereditary coordination begins to operate. The inhibitory block is thus removed or unlocked. In this context,

the ethologist refers to the combination of stimuli which reacts on an IRM as a key stimulus. The term is misleading in so
far as it suggests that only one stimulus is ever involved. This
obtains only in the rarest instances. Almost without exception
the key stimulus consists of a relatively complex plurality of
stimuli.

To the ant lion and web-spinning spider, a more or less characteristic form of vibration represents a key stimulus. The ant
lion lurks at the bottom of its sand crater. If an earthbound
insect crawls into the trap, its efforts to escape cause grains of
sand to trickle to the bottom of the crater. The ant lion
promptly shoots sand upward, creating a sort of avalanche which
hastens the insect's progress to the bottom of the crater. If a
few grains of sand are dislodged with a blade of grass, the ant
lion responds with the same reaction. The spider, in its turn,
responds to the vibration of its web and hurries to overpower
the captive insect which has caused it. Touch the web with a
vibrating tuning fork and the spider will respond in the same
way.

In the Indian Ocean, Eibl and I were able to observe how
the scent of blood induces deliberate searching movements in
sharks. Certain sea snails are roused by the perception of substances excreted by predatory starfish. Male silk moths find a
key stimulus in a sexually attractive substance secreted by the
female, to which they are extraordinarily sensitive and respond
at a great distance. To certain moths the ultrasonic echo-
sounding cries of the bat are a key stimulus which prompts
them to perform special evasive maneuvers such as banking or
diving. A simple optical key stimulus is the speckled pattern
on herring-gulls' eggs. As Kruijt ascertained, these gulls will not
roll eggs back into their nests unless this marking is present.
Far more complicated and difficult to define, by contrast, is the
stimulus pattern which prompts kittens, chicks, kids, and lambs
to halt on the edge of a sudden drop. That this also depends on
optical perception is demonstrated by the fact that they still
come to a halt when the drop is covered with a sheet of glass.

Some reflexes can be activated by a wide variety of stimuli
and are therefore termed unselective. Other reflexes respond
to a very specific stimulus and are called selective. The

same applies to IRM's. One example of an IRM which responds very unselectively—or, to preserve our original metaphor, can be opened with a wide variety of keys—is the one which activates prey-catching behavior in the toad. As soon as the young toad has developed from the larva, it snaps—if hungry—at all small moving objects within reach. Since these are mostly insects, the young toad does not fare badly. It also snaps at moving leaves or stones, however, and does not learn until later how to distinguish inedible objects and insects which taste objectionable or sting. This is an additional faculty which it acquires only by experience. The innate element in its behavior is wholly unselective. It begins by snapping every little moving body in exactly the same way, whereas every large moving body activates another hereditary coordination, namely, that of flight.

The toad reacts just as unselectively at mating time when faced with the task of finding a mate. The male leaps indiscriminately at any moving body and embraces it. Should the object of its attentions be another male toad, the latter emits a rapid series of cries, whereupon the former releases its hold. The mating-minded toad sooner or later encounters a female, whose spawn it fertilizes, but it has no innate "image" of a prospective mate. Waggle your finger in front of a male toad and it will mount and embrace it in exactly the same manner.

In order to discover what characteristics go to form a key stimulus, the ethologist uses what he calls a dummy, or decoy. This consists of the simplest possible reconstruction of the appropriate stimulus situation. Judicious alteration of a dummy or the addition of further characteristics enables one to ascertain what the IRM under examiniation responds to. In young blackbirds, food begging can be stimulated by a dummy consisting of two circular disks of black cardboard, one large and one small. The young birds construe the larger disk as their parent's body and the smaller one—at which they point their gaping beaks—as the head. In the male fence lizard the blue stripe on the edge of its belly arouses fighting behavior in other males. Females have no such marking and are not attacked, but paint the blue pattern on a female and she will be attacked at once. Paint out the stripe on a male and it will be courted

Dummy for the stimulation of food begging in young blackbirds. (*After Tinbergen and Kuenen, 1939*)

instead of attacked. A bunch of red feathers is enough to arouse fighting behavior in a male robin. Thus the word "mechanism" does possess justification here. The hereditarily fixed nerve structure responsible for recognition reacts like an automaton—in this sense, mechanically.

How little such reactions are associated with intelligence was shown by experiments with turkeys. To the turkey hen, the characteristic cheeping of turkey chicks is the key stimulus which arouses brood-tending behavior. Conceal a loudspeaker which emits this cheeping sound inside a stuffed polecat—one of the turkey's natural foes—and the turkey hen will take it protectively under her wing. Deprive the turkey hen of her hearing, on the other hand, and she will kill her own young because the appropriate key stimulus fails to reach her IRM.

Of all the very numerous key stimuli, ethologists have taken a particular interest in one group which Lorenz, to whose pioneering investigations most of such research can be traced, has given the name "releasers." The peculiarity of key stimuli of this type consists in the fact that they not only release behavior patterns *de facto* but *are bound* to release them. They are signals conducive to understanding between members of the same species or animals of different species which are on "friendly" (symbiotic) terms with one another. Thus, they are releasers par excellence and are known as signal stimuli. In their case, unlike that of other key stimuli, there is a clear tendency for their emission to be as distinct and conspicuous as possible.

The following point should be borne in mind here: If predators can recognize animals of species A by means of a certain key stimulus, such animals are at an obvious disadvantage. It follows, in the course of evolution, that the members of the species which maintains—and, consequently, propagates—itself more efficiently are those in which the key stimulus dwindles most or is not emitted at all. Natural selection here demands an involution of the distinguishing features in question. Conversely, when a key stimulus aids mutual recognition—as, say, in the case of mating partners—it is beneficial to the species if this signal becomes as distinct as possible. This sets off a contrary selective process which gains strength in the course of evolution.

As in every transmitter-receiver relationship, releasers are dependent upon being as simple, unmistakable, and infrequent as possible. The simpler they are, the simpler need be the receiving apparatus and the less the effort involved. The more unmistakable they are, the fewer failures of communication; and the more infrequent they are, the smaller the risk that other animals will use the same signal and so give rise to dangerous misunderstandings. Quite simple spatial relationships between visual characteristics play a part here, as Tinbergen was able to demonstrate in the case of the stickleback. The red belly of the male stickleback acts on other males as an aggression-releasing characteristic. Show the fish a wax sausage which has been painted red on the underside but bears no other resemblance to a fish (no fins or eyes) and it will be attacked no less fiercely. Turn the sausage over, however, so that the red paint is on top, and the dummy ceases to elicit aggressive behavior. In this instance the releaser is not simply "red" but "red underneath," as Tinbergen phrased it.

Different key stimuli can elicit the same form of behavior, and experiments with dummies enable one to present these to the subject separately. The males of one cichlid genus—they are blue with a black marking on their dorsal and ventral fins —confront their adversaries broadside on with fins spread, then aim tail strokes at their heads, and finally ram them with jaws open. Blue coloring and fin markings, transverse position, spread fins, tail strokes, and ramming technique—all these are key stimuli which, if presented separately, provoke a highly threatening reaction. The strongest reaction is observable in response to a combination of them all. Seitz, who was the first to recognize this, termed it the *Reizsummenphänomen*, or accumulated stimulus phenomenon. In many cases the ratio of effectiveness could even be accurately recorded in numerical terms.

Another discovery was that dummies can often be devised which surpass the efficacy of natural key stimuli. Koehler and Zagarus found that a ringed plover will abandon its own eggs in favor of one four times as large, even though it has no hope of hatching it. The cuckoo, as everyone knows, lays its eggs in other birds' nests, where its young are actually given preferential treatment by the unfortunate foster parents. This is attributable to the young cuckoo's wider throat, which acts as a stronger feeding release. Tinbergen and his associates established that the male brown butterfly prefers black female dummies to those of natural coloring. And for another species of butterfly, the silver washed fritillary, a rotating cylinder adorned with brown stripes running lengthwise, holds an even stronger sexual attraction than the sight of a female of its own kind. The ethologist refers in such cases to supernormal dummies.

Movements which initially served quite different purposes not infrequently developed into releasers. In gregarious ani-

Supernormal dummy. An oyster catcher abandoning its own egg in favor of an outsize artificial egg, although quite incapable of hatching it. (*After Tinbergen*)

mals, for instance, skin-tending motions became signals of contact readiness for the eliciting of a friendly attitude from members of the same species. When a dog licks us in greeting, this is a friendliness-eliciting signal which developed from mutual fur cleaning among the dog's ancestors and has now been extended to human beings. Jane Goodall observed that chimpanzees living in the wild in Tanganyika greet each other by means of embraces and lip contact. These releasers of friendly behavior in others very probably stem from hereditary coordinations of the mother-child relationship (hugging the maternal neck and mouth-to-mouth feeding).

The same movement can possess quite different releaser functions in different species. Tail wagging, which signifies friendly excitation in the dog and hostile in the cat, has become a releaser of friendly behavior in the first instance and a means of intimidation, or releaser of fear in an adversary, in the second. Just as it is a matter of pure convention what significance we attach to this or that particular word in human speech, so, in hereditarily determined animal signals, no essential importance attaches to their individual nature or mode of origination. All that is important is that they are understood. There must thus develop, on the one hand, a hereditary coordination linked with signals of particular significance and, on the other, a receptive mechanism capable of activating a particular reaction in response to such signals.

The courtship rituals performed by numerous creatures are designed not only to aid mutual recognition but to break down an equally innate fear of physical contact between mates. Courting is usually done by the male, though in many families, e.g., the *Syngnathidae*, the contrary is true. Prospective mates are prepared for copulation by a special form of "impressive" behavior and by numerous forms of display. Stimulative structures often develop within the context of this function. Male frigate birds, for example, impress their females by inflating a vivid red throat sac. Birds of paradise have developed peculiarly gorgeous plumage which they display in the most bizarre postures. Many fish don a wedding dress in that they become brilliantly discolored prior to mating. Among Australian bowerbirds, the male prefaces the act of copulation by constructing a special love bower which it decorates with flowers or brightly colored stones, then lures the female inside by means of courtship dances or other display behavior. The satin bowerbird goes to the lengths of painting its bower, applying a mixture of chewed berries and saliva with its beak or, sometimes, with a leaf or fragment of bark. The essential—and novel—element in assessing all these procedures is that in every case intensified key stimuli are presented in order to elicit innate reactions from members of the same species (or, in the case of symbiosis, from those of another species). They are not, therefore, purely unilateral signals but a means of actively influencing the reactions of others.

While observing intraspecific battles between rival males, Lorenz discovered the so-called appeasement gestures—special postures which the defeated animal adopts in order to dissuade the victor from doing it further injury. These are releasers which activate an inhibitory mechanism and render the victor simply incapable of further aggression. For reasons which must be more fully discussed at a later stage, intraspecific fighting possesses a biological importance which accounts for its development in the course of evolution. On the other hand, natural selection encouraged forms of combat in which members of the same species did not injure themselves seriously. Ethologists speak of jousting in this context, and a certain resemblance to man's sporting contests really does exist. As in them, there is an established ceremonial with certain rules of war—though these are innate. An individual worsted in such a contest adopts an appeasement position (among iguanas from the Galápagos, for instance, the loser lies down flat in front of its adversary), "pacifies" the victor, and can then retire unscathed. Signal stimuli not only elicit movement, therefore; many of them activate an inhibitory mechanism which prevents a movement from occurring.

The development of releasers from other movements and their improvement in the sense of increased efficiency is known in the field of behavioral research as ritualization. One can trace the course of such a development in the black woodpecker. While preparing itself a hole in a tree, it produces a drumming noise. A quite similar drumming noise becomes a signal warning other males not to trespass on its territory. The noise meaning woodpecker at work thus developed into the threatening signal, "I'm at work here—keep out!" In the case of cichlids, which invariably practice brood tending, one can trace the development of a similar signal. Among members of one branch of this family of fish, parents elicit a following reaction from their young by performing a peculiarly exaggerated swimming motion. The obvious significance of this is: "Watch out, children. I'm moving on now, so follow me!" Members of the genus *Aequidens* have developed the motion into an exaggerated wriggling movement performed for a short distance. This being even more striking and unusual, the likelihood that young fish may be misled by similar behavior in other fish becomes even smaller. Finally, among dwarf cichlids, we find an enticement motion in the form of exaggerated head shaking. Viewed in isolation, the origin of this signal would be hard to interpret. Comparison with related species of fish permits one to infer that this, too, is a last gestural relic of the swimming-on-ahead movement—in other words, a piece of exceptionally advanced ritualization.

Knowledge of such factors has helped to explain many mysterious procedures. The male empid or dancing fly *Hilara sartor*, for instance, gives the female a "wedding present" in the shape of a balloonlike cocoon. The highly aggressive female busies herself with this gift, and the male seizes the opportunity to copulate with her. What is the significance of this cocoon? Comparison with other dancing flies teaches us that this, too, is the terminal phase of a ritualizing process. Originally—as is still true today of the *Empis tessellata*—a small insect was proffered as a wedding gift. The female takes the insect, sucks it dry—and is simultaneously mounted. In other species the males spin a veil around the gift before presenting it, thereby turning it into a sort of parcel. The females strive to open the parcel— and the mating process takes places. In still other species only an empty cocoon is presented, and in the case of *Hilara sartor* this is a loose and quite transparent structure. Here, too, surviving species which have remained at this or that stage of development illustrate the course of evolution. The signals have become simplified but retain their activating effect.

Parallel with such ritualizations, parts of the body which participated in signaling movements became larger and more conspicuous. Since the signal stimulus gained in strength as a result, modifications of this kind—if they occurred in successive generations—also possessed selective value. Some snakes, for example, vibrate their tails as a threatening gesture. Although this was probably a quite general concomitant of excitation at first, it developed into a signal designed to intimidate adversaries. The rattlesnake, as a further improvement, developed horny rings which make a noise when its tail is vibrated and so emphasize the signal still more. In the porcupine, which erects its quills as a threatening gesture and also shakes its tail, an analogous development modified certain quills into noise-producing organs. The most surprising development of this type is to be found in the spotted hyena, which lives in packs and presents its erect penis as a gesture of appeasement and ceremonial greeting. Since the females did not possess such an organ, they could not perform this gesture. However, they carried their conformance with ritual so far that they, too, have developed a penislike organ which is erectile and enables them to greet their own kind in the male manner. From a purely external point of view, it is quite impossible to distinguish between male and female members of this species.

We began with the question of how organisms are in a position to perform their innate movements at the proper place and time. It has been shown that special nerve structures, also innate, are responsible for accomplishing this. They are able to select very specific combinations of stimuli from a multitude of sensory messages, and whenever such combinations occur, they release the corresponding hereditary coordinations.

4

Instinct and Mood

THE classic reflex theory postulated that a particular stimulus always elicited a particular reaction. Where instinctive behavior in animals is concerned, however, the position is not so simple. Quite different factors are at work here, and this brings us to a field of inquiry which is of especially great importance to the assessment of human behavior.

As we have already noted, the motor cells which control hereditary coordinations are constantly active. They produce an almost steady flow of coordinated impulses, which are normally prevented from reaching the muscles by the IRM's. Only when the appropriate key stimulus has effected its release can the movement run its course. If a hereditary coordination is not released for a considerable period—if the animal encounters no key stimulus—this can engender mounting excitation. The animal grows restless and starts actively to seek the liberating stimulus situation. This is what the phenomenon we refer to as instinct really is. In such a state of excitation, far weaker key stimuli than usual suffice to elicit the appropriate instinctive action. If the animal fails to find even these, the hereditary coordination can sometimes operate without any stimulus or incentive whatsoever—spontaneously, in fact. The inhibitory block is thrust aside, and the "lock" springs open without the requisite key.

Lorenz observed this in a starling which he had reared indoors. The bird received sufficient food but had no chance to work off its flying and insect-hunting coordinations. It accordingly indulged in the following behavior at regular intervals: It flew from its perch and snapped—although the room was completely insect-free—at thin air; then, returning to its perch, it performed the movements typical of insect killing and, finally, swallowed. Analogous behavior occurred in geese which Lorenz fed with grain on dry land. Although replete, they still showed an impulse to enter the water and upend at random. In both cases the birds' stomachs were full, so they could not have been hungry. Despite this, they obeyed an urge to perform particular movements spontaneously, without the need to eat, and obviously for the sole purpose of activating the appropriate hereditary coordinations.

A creature's increasing readiness to perform a particular instinctive action is described by the ethologist as a specific inclination or appetency. These burgeoning appetencies can be recognized externally by certain characteristic movements which are known as movements of intent. The creature, made restive by one of its instincts, suggests by the nature of its movements which of its innate motor patterns is agitating for release. A greylag goose, for example, when in "takeoff mood," performs aiming motions with its head for a period before taking the air. In the case of food-minded sharks in the Indian Ocean, Eibl and I observed that they moved their heads from side to side as though actually dismembering their prey.

Surrogates, or substitutes, are also employed as a means of working off appetencies. This can be seen in creatures which live in communities and among which the mutual grooming of fur and skin forms part of the innate behavior repertory. Keep such creatures in isolation and they will lack the opportunity to carry out these actions. Hence, they will often invite their keeper to let himself be groomed by them. Again, female rats are in such a strong retrieving mood ("retrieving" is the term applied to the instinctive act of salvaging young which crawl out of the nest) for some days after giving birth that they frequently use their own tail or one of their hind legs as a surrogate. They pick up their tail, carry it into the nest, and deposit it there; or they grip one of their hind legs and hobble back with it on three legs as if it were a baby rat.

Zoos afford a demonstration that the same impulses often occur in varying strength among different species of animals. Lions, for example, exhibit a weaker urge to move than wolves, a fact which stems from their dissimilar ways of life. Wolves bring down their prey by tracking and pursuit, whereas lions usually lurk in hiding until a suitable quarry approaches. Thus the lion does not mind if it obtains food without exertion in captivity. Its instinctive control is adjusted to a correspondingly quiescent mode of existence. With the wolf, food satisfies hunger but not the locomotive appetency normally associated with the acquisition of food. It thus paces restlessly up and down its cage in order to work off its pent-up excitation.

Spitz and Ploog observed a similar state of affairs in children. If babies sucked a given quantity of milk from a bottle in twenty minutes, they fell asleep peacefully. If the teat aperture was enlarged so that they could imbibe the same quantity in half the time, they showed their dissatisfaction by continuing to suck and by crying. Their hunger was assuaged, but their appetency for sucking had not been fully realized. If they were given the empty bottle, they continued to suck for another ten or so minutes and only then were satisfied. Bucket-fed calves offer a similar example. They develop the habit of sucking other calves or the rings on their stall chains.

Creatures in an appetitive condition become less receptive to key stimuli which elicit other behavior patterns. A hunting-minded animal must be presented with far stronger sexual stimuli before it makes the transition to mating behavior, and vice versa. As soon as the most pressing impulse has been satisfied, however, the animal regains its normal receptivity to other stimuli.

Lorenz speaks of a "parliament of instincts"—an extremely graphic metaphor. Just as members of a legislative body compete to submit their proposals and put them into effect, so instincts jostle for a chance to take the floor and issue their coordinated commands. They wait to take charge of the body and control it. If no such opportunity presents itself, heightened excitation results: The instinctive act in question becomes easier to elicit and can even take place at random and without special incentive.

Lorenz compares this process of mounting excitation with a liquid gradually rising inside a vessel until it finally overflows. Tinbergen and von Holst also refer to the internal damming of energy specific to action until it eventually spills over. Another graphic idea used to illustrate this process was borrowed from physiology, which speaks of a lowering or raising of stimulus thresholds. The higher a threshold, the harder it is to cross, and the same metaphor has been applied to stimuli which elicit instinctive actions or reflexes. A rise in the stimulus threshold signifies that correspondingly stronger stimuli are required to elicit the appropriate reaction. A fall entails that a relatively small stimulus can cross the threshold and eliminate the block.

Many ethologists have investigated the factors responsible for lowering the inhibitory stimulus threshold in particular forms of instinctive behavior—in other words, for prompting the emergence of particular instincts. Exhaustive inquiries showed that disregarding the spontaneous arousal of excitation, a creature's specific inclination is also affected by external and internal factors.

Thus—to quote an external influence—it is lengthening hours of daylight that put the male stickleback into a procreative mood. The responsible "member" in its parliament of instincts starts to wield influence and causes it to be assailed by a definite restlessness. As yet, the fish neither dons its mating garb nor exhibits any courtship or aggressive behavior. Sticklebacks migrate in shoals from their deep winter quarters to warmer, shallower waters. Once there, every male seeks a weed-stocked spot and establishes its territory. Only then does it put on mating dress and become receptive to other stimuli. If sticklebacks are captured during migration and placed in a basin which contains no plant life of any kind, they remain in a shoal and do not change color, simply because none of the males can mark out a territory of its own. Plant some weed in one corner, on the other hand, and one of the males will soon detach itself from the rest, take up station there, establish its territory, change color, and become procreatively inclined. In this case, therefore, the growth of procreative inclination is brought about by two factors of an external nature: first, lengthening hours of daylight; and second, the discovery of plants which lend themselves to the establishment of a territory (and nest building). As a result of these external stimulus situations, the "member of parliament" in the stickleback's central nervous system responsible for sexual behavior gains influence and assumes control of the body to an increasing extent, while other members are obliged to take a secondary role for the time being.

One example of an internal influence is the operation of hormones. It has been ascertained that when the female collared turtledove sights a displaying male, its ovaries release progesterone into the blood. The effect of this hormone is to arouse a disposition to brood somewhere between five and seven days later. Lehrmann, who experimented with eighty pairs of these doves, injected them with progesterone seven days before bringing the males and females together. When he offered them eggs at the same time as he brought them together, the pairs immediately embarked on brood-tending activities, which they would not normally have done. This was yet another instance of the ease with which instinctive behavior can be distorted and diverted from its natural course—in other words, of its rigidly mechanical nature. In this case, inclination was induced by a hormone. Introduce this into the bloodstream prematurely, and the instinctive member gains ascendancy correspondingly early.

Other instincts represent a further internal influence on the individual instinct. As we have already noted, the growth of an appetency renders a creature less receptive to other key stimuli. More precisely, a fall in one stimulus threshold raises the stimulus thresholds of other instincts. As the ethologist puts it, one instinct suppresses another, and there are numerous examples of such suppression. In birds, for instance, the inclination to brood substantially raises the stimulus threshold of flight behavior. Flight is harder than usual to induce when a bird is brooding—a fact for which the above line of reasoning provides a concrete and mechanical explanation. Similarly, repugnance can suppress a hen's willingness to peck for food. Obvious as this may seem, it is attributable to certain very specific reroutings in the bird's central nervous system. If a hen gets something objectionable in its beak, this can—depending on the strength of the stimulus—result in as many as four innately fixed reactions. It stops eating, extends its neck, makes movements with its tongue, and excretes saliva. If the aversion is very strong, it shakes its beak. Finally, it wipes its beak on the ground. Even if the bird performs only part of this motor sequence, its appetency for eating will—as quantitative experiments have shown—be diminished.

Inclination toward one form of instinctive behavior can, however, enhance the inclination toward another. When this happens, the ethologist says that the two instincts are positively correlated. Many creatures with an urge to eat can simultaneously experience an increased urge to fight. One very interesting point to note is that this correlation need not be common to males and females of the same species—indeed, that it can be diametrically opposed. In the male cichlid, for example, the flight mood suppresses preparedness for sexual behavior—that is to say, the fish loses interest in females when frightened. Aggressive inclination, on the other hand, is positively correlated with sexual behavior. In other words, if the fish is aggressively inclined, its preparedness for sexual behavior is intensified. In the female, the situation is reversed. If the female is fear-inclined, this can actually lead to an intensification of its preparedness for sexual behavior. Conversely, mounting aggressivity causes a diminution of sexual preparedness—that is to say, an aggressively inclined female is uninterested in sex. A similar difference between male and female behavior has been observed in other creatures as well.

Many hereditary coordinations, too, have an affinity to the extent that several of them combine to build up one form of instinctive behavior. A cat's preying behavior, for instance, involves the hereditary coordinations of lurking, stalking, pouncing, leaping, and fishing. These are performed in a definite order and thus influence one another. On the other hand, each such hereditary coordination has its own appetency. A cat which has lacked the opportunity to perform one or another of these actions for some time will search for a suitable stimulus situation, if only to be able to fish or pounce for the sake of so doing. The mouse thus becomes the object first of one and then of another procedure, and even a ball of wool can serve as a substitute.

On the basis of these and other observations, Tinbergen

formed the conclusion that individual instincts are constructed along hierarchical lines. The parliament of instincts comprises not only members but various ministries, each of which consists of a certain number of officials. These officials vary greatly in their relationship to one another, and each of them seeks to exercise independent authority—in other words, strives to control the body in a particular way.

What emerges from this is a picture of the animal organism which diverges from the traditional view. That which we habitually regard as a single unit breaks down into a number of authorities, each of which comports itself in a relatively autonomous manner. In terms of this picture, the body alone is a unit. It is not controlled by one key authority, however, but by hierarchically constructed ministries, one or another of whose ministers is always seizing power for brief periods.

Von Holst and von Saint-Paul acquired even deeper insights into this problem by cerebral stimulation in chickens. Having introduced electrodes into the brain by surgery, they were able to probe individual centers and stimulate them artificially by means of weak electric shocks. This enabled them to tell which form of behavior was controlling the current nerve structure. The tiny electrodes caused the birds no pain or discomfort. When they recovered from the anesthetic, they were completely unaware both of the electrodes and of the gossamer-fine wires emerging from their heads.

The results of these experiments in stimulation were very informative and are recorded in instructional films. One of these shows a cockerel seated contentedly on a laboratory table. Stimulation of a particular part of the brain ensues. At once, the cockerel stands up and starts to peck at the tabletop. There is nothing there to pick up, but as soon as the relevant spot is stimulated, the cockerel pecks like an automaton. Stimulation of another spot results in the cockerel's remaining seated but looking around. When the voltage is increased (approximately from .1 volt to .3 volt), the bird stands up and starts to cluck. A further increase in voltage and it walks about and evacuates. Yet another increase and it turns around, squats down, and points its beak in a certain direction. Finally, at about .9 volt, it takes off, emitting a series of cries. In this case, gradually increased stimulation elicited various hereditary coordinations in regular succession. In fact, the cockerel exhibited all the behavior patterns with which it would normally have greeted a potential invader of its territory. When von Holst stimulated the calm, seated cockerel with .9 volt right off, the intermediate phases disappeared and the bird flew off screeching. If he stimulated the same points several times, the result was exhaustion and a raising of the stimulus threshold such as can be observed under natural conditions.

Von Holst and von Saint-Paul were able to induce almost any hereditary coordination in poultry by artificial means. It turned out that many hereditary coordinations can be activated from a variety of points in the brain. One example was clucking and another walking. These hereditary coordinations occupy a very subordinate position within the hierarchy of instinctive movements and come into operation in the course of various behavior patterns. For instance, clucking is a concomitant of brood-tending behavior, as well as of the activated urge to flee. Again, the hen walks, or takes steps, not only when in quest of food but also during aggressive action and copulation. Lorenz christened these very simple hereditary coordinations "tool activities" because they are useful for various purposes. It is evident that the circuits in the brain are so disposed that various instincts make use of these basic movements, each within the context of its particular motor flow.

Simultaneous stimulation of different points enabled von Holst and von Saint-Paul to explore more fully the phenomenon of correlation, which we have already discussed. By means of such double stimulation they established that seven different permutations occur in response to the activation of different instincts. Two movements can, first, be *superimposed*—for example, simultaneous stimulation of the points responsible for pecking and head turning can result in the bird's pecking and turning its head at the same time. Second, two movements can *compromise*—for example, stimulation of "observing" and "looking around" (for danger) can cause the chicken to perform both movements but with halved intensity. Third, stimulation of "looking around" and "eating" leads to *vacillation*, or a condition in which the bird alternately eats and keeps watch.

Fourth, simultaneous stimulation of "turn right" and "turn left" can produce *neutralization*—the bird's head turns neither right nor left but remains centered. Fifth, simultaneous stimulation of two impulses can induce a *transformation* whereby the two stimulated impulses release a third, so that the bird performs an entirely different movement: "Pecking" and "escape," stimulated simultaneously, can produce deterrent screeching. Sixth, one impulse can *suppress* another, so that simultaneous stimulation elicits one form of behavior in full and only a vague suggestion of the other (in conjunction with the first). Seventh, one impulse can wholly *inhibit* another so that only the dominant partner appears in response to double stimulation.

Similar experiments in cerebral stimulation have since been carried out by other authorities. One noteworthy discovery concerns rats which were trained to carry out their own cerebral stimulation by depressing a key. A spot in the brain had been found which the animals clearly enjoyed stimulating. One rat, which stimulated itself more than 50,000 times in a twenty-four-hour period, became positively addicted to this particular stimulus and released it almost incessantly.

One phenomenon which has not been altogether explained is that completely aimless behavior patterns occur in animals under conditions of conflict. For example, fighting cockerels whose flight tendencies have been activated by their adversaries start to peck at the ground. Nothing could be less likely than that they should wish to seek food at this juncture, yet they go through the appropriate motions. Tinbergen ascribed this to an energy surplus which finds no outlet and consequently jumps to another nerve track. His name for this often observed process was displacement. It is also possible, however, that this phenomenon is attributable to the transformation noted by von Holst, whereby the simultaneous activation of two impulses releases a third. We shall revert to such movements in greater detail when discussing human gestures.

Lorenz adduced numerous examples to show how instincts—like the organs of a living creature—adapted themselves to changing environmental conditions in the course of evolutionary history, and how they were also molded by natural selection. Interestingly enough, instincts often showed themselves to be more rigid and "conservative" than the organs with which they operated. The ancestors of the modern stag, for instance, had no antlers but a considerably more effective set of teeth with which to defend themselves. In their case the purposive movement of teeth grinding developed into a warning signal. Fossil discoveries show that the strongly developed canines underwent gradual involution as time went by, and today stags defend themselves with their hoofs and antlers. The instinctive movement of teeth grinding was retained as a threatening signal, however, and thus showed itself more conservative than the organs on which it depended.

Lorenz verified substantial modifications of instinct in domestic animals. By protecting them from their natural foes and the rigors of the climate, man influenced natural selection by a process known as domestication. In the realm of movement, Lorenz found that long chains of hereditary coordinations disintegrated as domestication progressed: In other words, dedifferentiation took place. Many innate releasing mechanisms (IRM's) likewise lost their selectivity, that is to say, no longer responded to key stimuli with the same precision in domestic animals as in the wild species from which they were descended. In their case, the "lock" of instinctive action can be opened by many more "keys." Instincts themselves changed, too. Many of them, *e.g.*, the social instincts which help to keep animal communities together, regressed. Others, those of eating and mating, gained strength or became hypertrophied.

Similar forms of instinctive decay have also occurred in the course of natural evolution. Not only were they of great importance, but they formed a prerequisite of the learning process which we are about to discuss, for the higher vertebrates could acquire increased adaptability only by developing a less rigid innate structure. Only because their rigid hereditary fixations partly disintegrated were these creatures able to improve their behavior by learning. To quote Whitman, one of the earliest pioneers of behavioral research, failures of instinct were the open door by which individual experience could "enter" the animal and modify its behavior.

5

Acquired Behavior

IT does not appear difficult, at first glance, to draw a sharp distinction between innate and acquired behavior. The difference is clear from their very designations alone, or so one would think But, as this chapter aims to show, in practice it is extremely difficult to draw such a distinction.

We have already seen that innate behavior is controlled by nerve structures whose composition is determined by the hereditary formula inherent in a creature's chromosomes. The chromosomes do not, therefore, exercise direct control over hereditarily fixed behavior but merely create the mechanisms which contribute to such control. This is not the case with acquired behavior. This, too, is operated from the central nervous system but by nerve structures which the organism builds up as a result of personal confrontations with its environment. The controlling structures may be similarly constituted in each case—and there is much evidence to suggest that they are quite similar—but they come into being in quite different ways.

In the case of acquired behavior, we call the process by which they come into being learning. A distinction is drawn between various forms of learning, although they do not permit clear-cut differentiation. First, there is a relatively passive process—the accumulation of experience—which depends upon the formation of conditioned reflexes (associations). Then there is active learning of the sort known as trial and error, in which the forming of associations also plays an important part. A third alternative is learning by imitation, a process which can be linked either with deliberate demonstration or with teaching through the medium of verbal communication.

Each case presupposes a basic aptitude: The central nervous system must somehow be in a position to store experiences. Particular environmental impressions must leave behind traces of some kind. An organism must somehow be able to note certain details of its struggle with environment. For this purpose it needs a faculty which, when more highly developed, we call memory.

This faculty, which must not automatically be equated with deliberate human recollection, has been tested in animals by means of training experiments. The degree to which unicellular organisms possess memory is still in dispute, but such a faculty has been clearly demonstrated in very primitive flatworms (planarians). Experiments with a cuttlefish proved that its memory retained an impression for 27 days. In the case of a trout, memory survived for 150 days, of a rat for fifteen months, and of a carp for as long as twenty months. In each of these cases a particular incident had left traces in the brain of the creature in question which affected its behavior for a given period.

Much controversy surrounds the question of how we ought to conceive of these memory traces (engrams) in practical terms —in other words, how the central nervous system stores such experiences. The original theory was that memory depends on morphological or chemical changes inside the nerve cells. According to Eccles, on the other hand, memory is based on electrical oscillatory cycles which are interrupted by a particular stimulus—*i.e.*, by a specific experience—and then resume their course.

The theory of chemical anchorage (molecular hypothesis) is supported by experiments conducted with planarians. These small worms were trained to perform a certain task (they are capable of such an achievement) and then cut in half. The regenerative capacity of the planarian is such that the forepart grows a new tail and the hindpart a new head. Ensuing experiments seemed to show that both new individuals—the one with the regenerated head included—could accomplish the task in question. This implied that changes effected by learning were not only of a material nature but distributed throughout the body. A still more astonishing experiment was conducted with rats. They were also schooled in a task and then killed. An extract from their brains was injected into the abdominal cavity of other rats, whereupon the latter apparently produced a higher success ratio when performing the task in question than before being so inoculated. Although these findings are in dispute, it now seems likely that memory is stored in special molecules—probably those of deoxyribonucleic acid (DNA molecules). This would be particularly interesting because these molecules also carry hereditary coordinations, which would confirm a conjecture made as long ago as 1870 by Hering to the effect that common features exist between memory and heredity, which he termed organic memory.

Further experiments indicated the existence of two forms of memory, short term and long term. That totally different phenomena are involved became clear from experiments with cuttlefish, in which the two faculties are located in different areas of the brain. In the case of goldfish, it was possible to prove that their short-term memory changes into long-term memory within an hour, and that the latter definitely depends upon the formation of protein. It is conceivable, therefore, that both theories of memory are correct. Short-term memory might depend upon an electrochemical oscillatory process within the nerve cells, and these oscillations could lead to the forming of a physical substance in which the memory trace remains anchored for a considerable period.

Let us now turn to the first form of learning: learning by the formation of conditioned reflexes. Such learning can result in entirely new reactions, but it often promotes changes or refinements in behavior which is already innate. This is how the toad, having initially snapped at small moving objects, learns to avoid insects which taste bad or sting. The unpleasant experience associates itself with the memory of such creatures' special characteristics, and the toad refrains from snapping at insects of similar appearance. The same applies to the young European polecat, which will initially chase only creatures that move. Only experience teaches it to recognize the motionless mouse as well. The learning of special routes requires the correct collation of numerous landmarks. When the digger wasp first leaves its hole in the ground it flies in a circle several times so as to imprint the neighborhood on its memory and thus learns its return route. Bumblebees afford an even better illustration of how this form of direction finding depends upon imprinted landmarks. If they encounter a conspicuous flower and return immediately to their nest, they can still find the same flower again readily. If, however, they meet a less readily visible flower, they make several circuits before returning home so as to plot the bloom's exact position in relation to certain landmarks. In each case learning is based on an association of distinguishing features. The innate mechanisms for the recognition of key stimuli thus become more selective, and the behavior of the individual becomes better adapted to the particular features of its environment.

Learning by trial and error plays a major role in the acquisition of physical aptitudes. In birds, for instance, the motor coordination of flying is hereditarily fixed—but only in basic outline. Real skill in navigation—especially the difficult art of landing—can be acquired only by practice. Young mammals learn many of their adult aptitudes in the course of play, of which we shall have more to say later. They gauge the potentialities of their own bodies by repeated experimentation, and so build up cerebral control formulas which later stand them in good stead. Innate behavior patterns are often refined and improved in the process. For example, the "killing bite" is innate in the European polecat, but the animal must first learn the proper method of applying it to the neck of its quarry (*e.g.*, a rat). This it does while playing with youthful contemporaries. Orientation problems, too, are solved by trial and error. This process has been exhaustively studied in mice, in artificial mazes in which food can be reached by a single specific route. After several fruitless attempts, the rodents stumble on the route by accident and finally, after repeated successes, register it. The guidance formula built up within their brain is then based on a whole system of distinguishing features—on acquired recognition of key stimuli which, when present in a certain sequence, elicit certain reactions.

Learning by imitation clearly requires special mental capacities, since this process is demonstrable only among the higher vertebrates. As soon as lion cubs are old enough to accompany their mother, they watch her hunting and thus learn how to stalk prey, keep to leeward, and perform outflanking maneuvers. It is well known that rats quickly learn to avoid poisoned bait. In this case, knowledge passes from one animal to another because the inexperienced take their cue from the experienced. Traditions can grow up among animals in this way. In England, titmice have learned how to use their beaks to open milk bottles left on doorsteps. This avian discovery was first observed at Swaythling, Hampshire, in 1921 and spread to many other parts of the British Isles—Scotland and Ireland included—in the twenty-six years that followed. The growth of a similar tradition was traced from individual to individual among macaco monkeys on the Japanese island of Koshima. The animals were fed by scattering grain on the seashore, which meant that the grains of wheat had to be picked out of the sand. One of the monkeys discovered that it was easier to separate grain from sand by throwing a handful of sand, complete with grain, into the water, where the components separated because the sand sank more quickly. This discovery, which took place completely free of human influence, was subsequently copied by other monkeys of the same community, and the expedient was adopted by no less than nineteen of them over a period of twelve years. In each of these cases the creatures in question had managed to introduce other individuals' motor coordinations into their own—a process which may seem simple to us but actually represents an extremely complex linking of sensory impressions with personal experiments in motion.

Learning by demonstration, an even rarer phenomenon in the animal world, is a faculty that seems to be confined to creatures of the highest intelligence. At Basel Zoo, Schenkel watched a mother gorilla lead her newborn baby to the bars of the cage, encourage it to climb by means of appropriate movements, and even assist it by guiding its paws. She was thus teaching it by encouraging some movements and inhibiting others—another process which seems obvious to us because we are conversant with it, but which, in the female gorilla, presupposes a very advanced and complicated feat of intelligence.

What we mean by intelligence or understanding is easier to illustrate by means of examples than it is to define theoretically. If a chicken sees an inaccessible cache of food behind a fence, it runs up and down behind the barrier and achieves nothing. A dog in similar circumstances soon "realizes" that this is pointless. It gains access to the food by examining the fence to see if it has an opening or can be bypassed. What we call intelligent behavior generally depends upon a better recognition of related factors. We are still ignorant of the particular cerebral processes which form the basis of this ability. In essence, however, they probably entail the evaluation of past experiences, acquired independently of one another, in such a way as to master a new problem as it arises.

An attempt was made to analyze such performances in specially constructed cages. The objects of research—mainly rats and mice, but also doves, cats, and monkeys—were encouraged to perform assignments by pressing keys or manipulating other contrivances, success being associated with a suitable reward. It became clear that initial successes achieved by random experimentation usually failed to make a lasting impression. A graphic evaluation of results shows that the learning curve rises very gently at first. After further successes, however, the number of correct actions increases notably as though the creature has suddenly grasped the nature of the task confronting it. In many intelligence tests the animals did not proceed at random even during preliminary experimentation, but in such a way as to suggest that they were working on the basis of a hypothesis. Depending on the fruits of success in earlier experiments, they would—when confronted by an intersection in a maze, for instance—either favor one of two turnings for a while or choose them alternately.

Numerous experiments have demonstrated that animals, too, have the ability to abstract. They are capable of recognizing the essential features common to different phenomena and thus—by abstracting certain relevant characteristics—arrive at concepts. These, however, differ from human concepts in that they are averbal, or not crystallized in the form of verbal definitions. Experiments conducted by Rensch and Dücker with a civet cat revealed a considerable ability to sift various sensory impressions for certain characteristics essential to the significance of the whole (generalizing abstraction). The animal was trained to distinguish between two parallel semicircles (meaning "food") and two straight lines (meaning "punishment"). It was then presented with increasingly complicated patterns in which these two recurred in modified form. The cat showed that it could eventually distinguish between the concepts "bent" and "straight." It also, in similar fashion, formed the twin concepts "equal" and "unequal."

When we remember the innate ability to select certain key stimuli from a plurality of stimuli and recognize particular objects by their distinctive features, the analogy with concept formation becomes obvious. What occurs through an innate

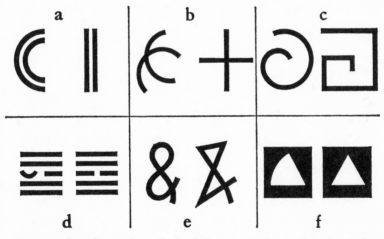

Patterns for the testing of averbal concept formation in a civet cat. The animal was trained to construe two parallel semicircles as positive (rewarded with food) and two parallel straight lines as negative (a). Once it had mastered these alternatives it was offered the elements "bent" and "straight" in an increasingly modified form. The percentage of correct choices was 90 percent in b, 90 percent in c, 82 percent in d, 80 percent in e, and 66 percent in f. (*After Rensch and Dücker, 1959*)

mechanism in one instance is effected in the other by a nerve structure founded on experience. Recognition of the common element by means of certain typical features is what is involved in each case.

Koehler recorded outstanding examples of generalizing abstraction while testing the abilities of various creatures to count. Doves, parrots, ravens, and squirrels learned to pick out a quite specific, prescribed number of seeds or morsels of food from a larger number of the same. In the case of a gray parrot the experimental procedure was rendered still more difficult by obliging it to take the seeds from several covered food bowls containing different numbers of seeds (and in one instance none at all). The bird proved equal to the task: It uncovered each bowl in turn and stopped after finding and eating the preordained number of seeds. More than that, it understood its orders just as well when the prescribed number was conveyed by means of light and sound signals. In other words, it had transferred the concept of number from light to sound.

Where such achievements are concerned, related factors are embodied in a form of complex. This particular faculty was exhaustively tested in maze experiments with rats and mice, which revealed an astonishing ability to transpose. For example, once mice had committed all the passages in a maze to memory, they could pick their way through another maze which resembled the first except that its passages met at an angle of 45 degrees, say, rather than at right angles. And they found their way around the new maze even when all distances were doubled—indeed, they succeeded even when the new maze represented a mirror image of the old.

The ability to grasp related factors is particularly marked in chimpanzees. These creatures can solve the problem posed by a suspended banana by stacking two boxes and mounting them armed with a stick. They are also capable of lengthening a stick by fitting two sections together. In Tanganyika Jane Goodall watched wild chimpanzees extracting termites from their nests with thin twigs or blades of grass. Using their fingers to open one of the exits used by termites at swarming time, they insert the twigs. This causes a number of termites to bite, whereupon the chimpanzees withdraw them on the end of the twigs and

Chimpanzees undergoing intelligence tests. Left: A chimpanzee
fishing for a banana with the aid of two crates and a stick. Right:
A chimpanzee preparing to reach a banana outside its cage by
fitting two rods together. (*After Koehler, 1921*)

eat them. Another feat of intelligence Jane Goodall also observed enables chimpanzees to get at water too deeply secreted
in hollow tree trunks to be reached with the mouth. Just as
we would employ a sponge, so they take a handful of leaves,
thrust their arms into the hole, dunk the leaves in the water,
and thus convey the liquid to their mouths. All these cases
exemplify a use of tools based on intelligent behavior.

The ability to form new and individual patterns of action
which are not hereditarily determined can thus be traced in animals as it develops, beginning with slight modifications in
innate forms of reaction and ending with genuine feats of in-

telligence which approximate our own. We can also trace the continuous expansion and differentiation of the central nervous system—in other words, the increasing refinement of the organ responsible for such feats. Quantitative as well as qualitative differences appear to be involved here. Rensch succeeded in establishing the existence of a relationship between vertebrates' performances in the field of learning and their absolute brain capacity. It would seem, therefore, that a part is played not only by the particular architectonics within the brain but also, and to a very large extent, by the absolute number of ganglion cells available.

As already mentioned during our allusion to animal concept formation, there are certain parallels between acquired and innate behavior. This becomes even clearer in the realm of movement. With hereditary coordinations we saw that the cells which provide their anchorage are characterized by a spontaneous generation of excitation, and that there is a growth of appetencies which compel the organism to perform certain movements. The same applies in this respect to coordinations acquired by learning, which may be termed acquired coordinations. Once engraved on the brain by frequent repetition, these become habits. And as one can plainly see in animals, habits are linked with appetencies, one expression of this being the restiveness which afflicts animals after the expiration of the time at which they are accustomed to perform an action. A dog which is used to retrieving, and which is given no opportunity to do so, plainly shows it. Here, too, there is a lowering of the stimulus threshold—and when the action cannot be carried out, displacement movements occur. The excitation caused by the blocking of a habit leads to the performance of other actions of some kind.

Although innate and acquired behavior may come into being in different ways, they do betray certain similarities. Distinguishing between them can be difficult, however. To take conditioned reactions as an illustration of this, it is innate in dogs that their salivary glands begin to function as soon as they perceive a certain taste. Ring a bell before feeding (this was Pavlov's classic experiment designed to prove the formation of conditioned reflexes) and before long the sound of the bell alone suffices to cause the secretion of saliva, even without the perception of taste. What is acquired and what is innate in this instance? The new nerve connection (association) is clearly acquired, but the new reflex also makes partial use of the old innate nerve track because no new nerve connection to the salivary glands has been formed. Thus, strictly speaking, only part of this new behavior is acquired.

In the case of complex movements the problem becomes even more difficult. Many hereditarily fixed behavior patterns are still incomplete at birth and do not mature until later, so that an animal may seem to have formed certain behavior as a result of some learning process or other. Instances of delayed maturation have been demonstrated in both the motor and sensory fields. One classic case is Hess' experiment with chicks. Soon after hatching, these begin to peck at small objects with their beaks, but in the first few days they usually miss the mark. Give them a target consisting of a slab of soft clay with a nailhead in the center, and one can clearly see from the imprint of their beaks how wide of the mark they are—*i.e.*, the extent of their "scatter." Their aim improves on the second and third days, and by the fourth day the imprints are close to the nailhead. It seems in this case that improved aim is the result of practice—in other words, acquired. Hess succeeded in showing that this is not so, however, and that what is involved is a late maturing of the directional mechanism. He provided newly hatched chicks with prismatic spectacles which gave their vision a slight bias toward the right. The chicks' beak imprints were displaced accordingly—that is to say, their scatter was centered not on the nailhead but some distance to the right of it. On the fourth day they were more concentrated but still to the right of the nailhead. The chicks had certainly not learned—in fact, the nailhead had not been struck once—but the scatter had become smaller. This clearly showed that their aiming mechanism had improved as a result of late maturing, not of a learning process.

The distinction between innate and acquired is further obscured in many forms of behavior by the fact that innate and acquired components are often closely conjoined or, as Lorenz puts it, entwined. For instance, the motivation for learning—

i.e., the reason why an animal troubles to learn at all—derives largely from its various instincts. This or that member gains predominance in the parliament of instincts, whereupon the animal exerts all its faculties in order to attain the goal dictated by its prevailing impulse. This form of endeavor is one of the chief reasons why an animal learns at all. What it learns is undoubtedly acquired, therefore, but the motive power is innate.

In addition, there is another special instinct which aims at learning for its own stake. This is the play or curiosity instinct which prompts the young of the higher vertebrates actively to explore their environment and test their physical ability by carrying out every conceivable type of movement. For the most part, hereditary coordinations are innately fixed in these animals only in the form of quite short series of movements—components which are subsequently built, by means of learning and practice, into more highly integrated and complicated motor patterns. The animals thus benefit from an ability to adapt themselves to environmental conditions far better than they could if dependent solely upon chains of action determined by heredity. Is behavior that comes into being in this way acquired, or is it innate? The answer is: both.

Experimenting with squirrels, Eibl ascertained the precise extent to which the concealment and opening of nuts may be ascribed to innate or acquired motor control. The act of concealment is entirely determined by heredity, whereas the technique of opening nuts comprises both acquired and innate components. The movements of gnawing and cracking are already present as hereditary coordinations, but the squirrel learns the best method of putting them into effect by experimentation. An expert can tell by the marks of gnawing on opened nuts whether an experienced or inexperienced squirrel has been at work. Inexperienced animals begin by gnawing crisscross grooves at random until the shell breaks open at some point. Experienced animals, by contrast, gnaw only one groove, insert their lower incisors in it for better purchase, and crack the shell open. Eibl noted that inexperienced squirrels also try to exert a leverage effect, but this yields results only when the groove is correctly aligned.

A further entwinement of innate and acquired behavior occurs in the so-called learning dispositions, which represent a kind of foreknowledge of what ought to be learned. Chaffinches, for example, have a song with an innately fixed length and number of syllables, but its characteristic division into three strophes must be learned by imitating adult members of the species. If young chaffinches reared in isolation are played recordings of other species of birds, they will accept their song as a model, but only if it resembles that of the chaffinch in tonal quality and strophic form. If they are played various songs including that of their own species, they will recognize the latter and give it preference as a model. In this instance, as in numerous others, the ability to learn is not entirely flexible but innately slanted in one particular direction. The creature has a prescribed curriculum, as it were—in other words, an innate knowledge of what it should learn.

Acquired behavior becomes still more firmly rooted as a result of imprinting, a phenomenon discovered by Lorenz. Here, learning dispositions make their appearance at a quite specific sensitive or critical period, and learning of this kind results in patterns of behavior which cannot subsequently be changed. Goslings, for example, become imprinted by what they see immediately after hatching out and follow it around from then on. Normally this is their mother, but if they catch sight of a human being or a balloon, they will follow only a human being or a balloon. Not even reunion with their mother will alter their behavior. They are henceforward imprinted in favor of another object, and their instinct to follow can be aroused only by that object. In this case the act of following is present as a hereditary coordination, but the nature of what is followed depends upon sensory impressions received during the early days of existence. Instinctive behavior is thus in part flexible. The motor component is complete, whereas the sensory component acquired its shape from a particular impression.

Hess determined the exact duration of this critical period in ducklings. He mounted a dummy drake on a disk which was rotated slowly while a loudspeaker concealed in the dummy emitted artificial calls. Having been kept in total darkness for varying periods, each of the ducklings was allowed to follow the dummy in a circle for one hour. Depending upon the strength of their impulse to follow, they faithfully scurried along after the dummy. By this means, Hess was able to determine that the critical period in ducks occurs between the thirteenth and sixteenth hours after hatching. Ducklings which followed the dummy during this period were henceforth imprinted in favor of its particular characteristics. They continued to prefer drakes, although ducklings are normally led by the mother duck, which has different coloring.

In many creatures, sexual behavior is also determined during sensitive periods. A male duckling which is made to associate exclusively with male ducks during the crucial period will behave homosexually for the rest of its life, even when females are in the vicinity. Similarly, a young cockerel in its sensitive phase can be imprinted in favor of ducks and will later wade into the water in order to court them. A jackdaw which is reared by humans until fully fledged and prevented from seeing other jackdaws remains sexually imprinted in favor of human beings. It may consort with other jackdaws, but when the mating season arrives a year later, it will only court human beings—even if there are other jackdaws around. In all these instances, imprinting must occur long before the creatures exhibit any sexual behavior. Budgerigars imprinted in favor of human beings can be induced to mate and breed in a covered cage. One sight of a human being, however, and both birds start courting the latter, pair formation is disrupted, and the brood neglected. Such examples are clearly illustrative of the power inherent in this process.

In many creatures even brood-tending behavior is influenced by imprinting. The cichlid *Hemichromis bimaculatus,* for instance, can distinguish between the young of its own species and those of another. It protects its own and eats the others. If alien eggs are put beneath it at first breeding, however, it will protect the young fish that hatch from them and also prefer the young of the same species to its own in future breeding periods.

Imprinting determines motor behavior as well as sensory. Heinroth discovered this in some nightingales which he reared. The young nightingales were within earshot while he was recording the song of some blackcaps; some months later, when their own song commenced in springtime, Heinroth was surprised to hear that they sang exactly like blackcaps, faultlessly and without omission. Similarly, if zebra finches hear nothing but young gulls during their first thirty-five days, they become imprinted by the gulls' totally alien call. Even if they consort continuously with their own kind thereafter, they still emit calls like young gulls and continue to do so.

It is interesting to note, finally, that serious behavioral disorders can occur in a creature if it is deprived in youth of certain environmental stimuli which are necessary to its normal development. Female rhesus monkeys, for example, proved to be poor mothers and extremely aggressive if reared apart from their own mothers. Their contact with other members of the same group was also impaired. Again, it is particularly important for young rhesus males to have playmates. If reared in isolation, they fail to copulate with females when adult because they grip them incorrectly. Significantly, they are incapable of learning the technique in later life. We speak here of learning processes which resemble imprinting. In this case, too, the formation of an innate behavior pattern is linked with the timely appearance of particular environmental stimuli.

Thus the question "Innate or acquired?" can be decided only on the basis of very careful investigation. Even acquired behavior may be largely influenced by a hereditary formula.

6

And What of Man?

W HAT of human beings? Do "animal" behavior patterns
still operate in our case? Are our forms of movement
and recognition hereditarily determined, too—in other
words, are we programmed in advance? Are we also impelled
and controlled by mechanisms within our brain which operate
without our even being aware of the fact?

This question is obviously of great importance to every individual human being. After all, each of us imagines himself to
be the possessor of an ego which controls his manifold actions.
If it turns out that our actions are partly programmed and thus
beyond the scope of our free will, it is certainly important to
know how these automatic controls function, how and on what
occasions they come into play, and how they can be influenced
should the need arise.

The information in the foregoing chapters indicates that the
study of animal behavior offers certain insights which can help
us view many phenomena of human behavior from new and
different angles. If we learn how, on the basis of innate cerebral structures, animals are encouraged in certain very specific series of actions and checked in others, we must be reminded of what we refer to as our own urges and inhibitions—
processes which often run counter to the true will of our ego
and of which we are not always in control. If we learn how specific inclination, in animals, is affected by external or internal
stimuli, or by spontaneous processes within the nerve cells, this

recalls how our own mood is often affected by environment—by other people, changes of scene, or the state of the weather; how processes within our bodies also play their part—illness, drugs, the physiological processes peculiar to menstruation in women, or the disinhibiting effects of alcohol; and how we are sometimes prone to moods which can substantially affect our actions without our being able to give any concrete reasons for them. If we hear how, in animals, appetencies emerge and stimulus thresholds simultaneously diminish—a process which leads to increasing restlessness and concentration upon the quest for fulfillment of some particular urge or other—we may be reminded how, in our own case, our perceptions are distorted when we are hungry, sexually aroused, or frightened; how we then, to an increasing extent, think exclusively of food, seek a mate, or see ourselves overwhelmed by dangers and difficulties. If we hear that excitation can "jump the track," we may be reminded of Freud's doctrine that, when man's sexual urge is denied an adequate outlet, this pent-up force or libido can sublimate itself into very different activities. If an economist considers the stimulus threshold and accumulated stimulus phenomenon, he may perhaps recall man's relationship to what he buys and may wonder if the laws propounded by Herman Gossen are not explicable in terms of just such a basic phenomenon. If we hear of the phenomenon of imprinting, we are again reminded of Freud and of psychoanalysis, which long ago indicated that adult behavior is determined during certain sensitive periods of childhood development. Finally, if we hear of hereditarily determined learning dispositions, our thoughts may return to Kant and the categories to which our mind is chained *a priori*—or, equally, to the subject of human customs and traditions. The question then arises whether these are merely fortuitous parallels, or whether the human mind, being hereditarily fixed, tends in just such directions.

So much for one side of the coin. The other is that we are to date virtually unable to pronounce upon the question of to what extent human behavior is hereditarily determined or influenced, simply because there has been almost no research in this direction. Human beings have hitherto been studied from another angle and the phenomena of our behavior considered with different questions in mind. Moreover, with human beings it is all but impossible to solve the problem of "innate or acquired?" by rearing individuals in isolation. The only such recorded experiment was conducted by Frederick II, the thirteenth-century ruler of Sicily, who wished to discover if Hebrew, Greek, or some other tongue were the primordial language of mankind. He arranged for a number of children to be reared by foster parents who were forbidden to address a word to them. The children died. Certain indications, but only of a limited nature, are afforded by congenitally blind and dumb children, who have great difficulty learning many things by experience. Cerebral stimulation, which might also prove informative, has only been tried in exceptional cases so far. One of the few methods of isolating the innate components of our behavior is to compare candid motion picture films of behavior patterns in various parts of the world. If such films display essential similarities, this would suggest the presence of an innate human behavior mechanism. Children have frequently been filmed unawares, but there is little similar documentation on adult behavior.

For all the definite parallels with animal behavior which exist, scientific pronouncements about them must remain purely speculative until research has produced concrete evidence. However, we cannot disregard the high probability that true functional relationships exist. Where the physical characteristics of animal organisms are concerned, there is ample evidence that their further development and modification were extremely gradual. Lorenz's experiments have shown that it was the same with instincts, though here the process of change may be accelerated by domestication. These biological facts speak for themselves. They render it highly improbable that basic attributes such as the main instincts have undergone any substantial change during the relatively short span of human evolution. In the case of man—particularly in view of his self-awareness, imaginative faculty, and superior capacity for learning—quite different conditions undoubtedly applied. On the other hand, it is extremely unlikely that man, at a single stroke, surmounted and transcended the whole of the animal heritage whose development can be traced to him.

As for reflexes, there can be little doubt that our organism is largely controlled by those that are already laid down by our hereditary formula. Wholly divorced from our consciousness, they regulate the functions of our internal organs and much of our behavior toward our environment. Heartbeat, respiration, blinking, and pupillary reflex are examples of such functions. With us, as with animals, many functions are controlled by regulatory cycles (that is, reflex feedback systems). We, too, exhibit reafference, the peculiarly complicated reflex system explored by von Holst. Only in the rarest instances— *e.g.*, respiration—can we also influence these reactions by an effort of will. Most of them are beyond our ken and control and in this sense form a sort of id rather than genuine ingredients of our psychic ego. Thus, far from being controlled by our ego, innate reflexes are the act of an id which is independent thereof.

That a parliament of instincts is at work within us, too, may be assumed with a high degree of certainty and should be apparent to each individual from personal experience. Thanks to our intellectual ability, however, an entirely new phenomenon supervened: Existing forms of innate and acquired behavior came under special control. Animals are governed by a ministry-like directorial hierarchy (acquired behavior patterns, too, being pressed into the service of the various instincts), whereas in man the missing "head of government" has been supplied. Our conscious processes of thought, deliberation, and inference represent a level of cerebral integration which is superior to other "departments." These we regard as our real ego, and it is their decisions, based on individual experience, which constitutes our free will proper. But how powerful is this authority? How far can it prevail against individual members of the parliament of instincts, given that "differences of opinion" arise? To what extent does this supreme authority ally itself with one impulse or another? Furthermore, with learning dispositions and imprinting, how free is our ego in its emergence, and to what extent is its development and evolution likewise determined and influenced by heredity?

It is especially evident with the sexual urge that this depends upon innate impulsion mechanisms and does not, for example, owe its origination to learning processes. Freud, himself, pointetd out that although capable of controlling, restraining and sublimating the sexual urge, human willpower can never wholly eliminate it. We will discuss other extremely powerful human impulses which are probably likewise innate in greater detail at a later stage. They, too, are characterized by an uncontrollable endogenous growth of excitation and will, if deprived of fulfillment, result in restlessness and an active quest for a "short-circuiting" stimulus situation. If that proves equally fruitless, it can lead, in man, to other phenomena of a partly pathological nature.

As might be expected, few hereditary coordinations are represented in man. It is a characteristic of the mammals—as opposed to birds, reptiles, and fish, which still possess long series of hereditary coordinations—that they have freed themselves from the restraints imposed by hereditarily fixed motor patterns, thereby gaining in adaptive modifiability. Mammals take correspondingly longer to develop, on the other hand, and this necessitates prolonged brood protection. Man, who has become the learner par excellence, requires a particularly long period of "brood tending."

Some hereditary coordinations are, however, detectable in man. The newborn baby comes equipped with the oral movements of sucking, with the search automatism which leads it to the mother's breast, with the ability to grip and cling, cough and cry. The basic movement of walking is innate in man, as becomes apparent when a newborn baby is held upright above a flat surface. It advances each foot in turn and will even describe climbing movements when confronted by a step. Expressive reactions such as trembling, turning pale, and uttering cries of pain are also innate in man, as are the rudiments of human facial expression, which will also be discussed at greater length in due course.

In the sensory realm, by contrast, human behavior appears to be influenced far more by innate mechanisms. For instance, we react very definitely to key stimuli in the field of chemical sensory perception. The ingestion of rotting substances or excrement is detrimental to our health, and we react unfavorably to them by reason of key stimuli in the olfactory domain. In the optical domain, fear reactions are elicited by darkness, steep drops, and large approaching bodies. These, too, are probably innate.

We do not know whether the various reactions of animals are linked with emotions similar to our own. Many observations suggest so, but this is not provable scientifically. Being unable to communicate with animals, we cannot make any pronouncement about their subjective sensations. In our own case, feelings of pleasure and displeasure—contentment or discontent, happiness or unhappiness—are linked with our various urges. If we can satisfy them, pleasant sensations accrue to us; if not, we suffer physically or "mentally."

Certain movements on the part of other human beings represent peculiarly strong key stimuli from our point of view. We speak here of a mood transmission effect, one very clear example being gestures conveying fear. If a man exhibits fear, he can transmit his fear to others. We feel incomparably safer in our modern world than the man of a 1,000 or 10,000 years ago, yet we still react acutely to signs of panic. Especially when we are standing in a dense crowd, a sudden move to escape will give rise to an urge to join in in a reaction which is certainly not the result of rational deliberation. Feelings of enthusiasm and joy are also transmissible, which is one essential reason why people are attracted to public festivities and mass entertainments. If we see other people eating (and are not completely satiated ourselves), our own appetite will be stimulated even if we have no desire to eat. If we see other people streaming in a certain direction, the spectacle arouses our own curiosity. If other people yawn, their weariness may transmit itself to us. Finally, the sight of looters racing through the streets has swept away many a man who would, under normal circumstances, have been utterly opposed to such behavior.

Lorenz gave an instructive example of our hereditarily determined response to releasers in his "baby face" diagram. When we find a young child cute or sweet—in our subjective estimation—we are responding to a number of very specific characteristics, peculiar to young children, which combine in accordance with the rules of the accumulated stimulus phenomenon. Lorenz lists the following characteristics under this

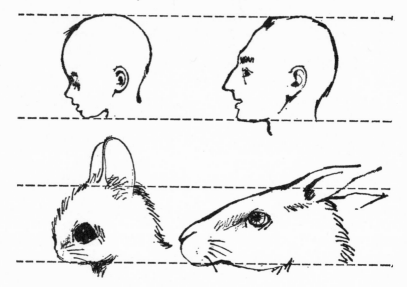

Lorenz's "baby face" diagram. In contrast to the proportions of the adult head, those of the child strike us as being "cute," and we transfer the same evaluation to young animals whose heads display similar characteristics. *(After Lorenz, 1943)*

heading: a relatively large and high-domed head, large eyes situated very low down, chubby cheeks, short plump extremities, and ungainly movements. We transfer this criterion to animals, too, and find them equally lovable and cute when they display similar characteristics. From the ethological standpoint, modern doll manufacture represents an intensive effort to produce effective dummies for the eliciting of these particular human reactions. Both in dolls and toy animals (one has only to think of Disney products) these effective characteristics are not only stressed but exaggerated, thereby creating supernormal dummies to which almost everyone responds.

Specialists in behavioral research likewise regard the female breast as a releaser—or to put it more crudely, a signaling apparatus. That the milk-yielding function is not decisive to the special development of this part of the female anatomy may be inferred from the fact that a small breast—as in the monkey—is quite sufficient for this purpose. Rather, the conspicuous shape of the female human breast acts as an effective pleaser upon the sexual proclivity of the male. Modern advertising and the history of fashion afford plenty of indications that man has succeeded in devising supernormal dummies in this field, too.

Going a stage further, Lorenz advanced the theory that our peculiar aesthetic sense can be traced largely to an innate evaluation of the basic proportions and characteristics of the human body. There is no doubt that our appreciation of beauty —when viewing a landscape, for instance—depends upon other basic factors as well, but there is equally little doubt that an innate recognition of the robust and well-proportioned human body plays an important part in such evaluations. If this is true, however, many questions must be differently formulated. The question "Why is this beautiful and that not?" becomes the quite different question "Why do we human beings regard this particular thing as beautiful and that as ugly?" This would mean that the explanation of the aesthetic phenomenon lies not in the form of the stimuli but in the formation of the nerve structures that receive them. Consequently, there would be no such thing as a beauty independent of human evaluation.

In an analogous way, Lorenz ascribes our moral sense to modes of reaction which are already innate in us. He points out that certain situations elicit very specific reactions from us, whether we like it or not. The maltreatment of a child or the bullying of a defenseless woman provokes a sense of outrage, whereas a man's self-sacrifice on behalf of his family, friends, or country tends to arouse our admiration. Lorenz further points out that we cannot prevent ourselves from reacting in the prescribed fashion even when such scenes are presented to us on film in an extremely crude—indeed, trashy—manner. Even when we watch them several times in succession we can observe a renewal of the same effect on each occasion. The reaction is quite automatic and uncontrolled. Lorenz attributes it to the workings of the social instincts which have grown up among human beings in the same way as they have done in a variety of social animals.

In our case—still according to Lorenz—these instincts are in the process of involution because of man's self-domestication, which means that he shields himself just as artificially against enemies and climate as he does his domestic animals. Although not as pronounced in us as in monkeys, these instincts still find clear expression in corresponding reactions.

This awkward yet interesting question sheds quite another light on the problem of human morality. Many religions, Christianity included, regard the human conscience as an innate faculty, but definitely not one that we share with animals. Indeed it is precisely this conscience, this inherent morality, which renders the thought of man's animal ancestry so unacceptable to so many people. They see this form of human evaluation as something unique. If it should turn out that it is not a human peculiarity—indeed, that impulses of this nature have actually become weaker in us than in the animals related to us—it would mean that currently accepted patterns of thought had been disrupted on a truly massive scale.

Publications dealing with behavioral research often present comparisons between man and beast which are not really valid and should therefore be rejected. For example, von Holst observed that with the wrasse—a fish which lives in shoals—a specimen will become the leader of its shoal if surgically deprived of its forebrain. The forebrainless fish is thereby disinhibited and loses its shoal-forming reactions. It swims where it pleases, and the shoal tags along behind it. Any account which concentrates on effect can logically thus assert: "You see, that's the way things are—the masses always follow the brainless ones!" It is not hard to see that this analogy will not stand serious examination. Wrasse shoals, in which no one fish has individual knowledge of another, are not susceptible of comparison with human communities, nor is it a criterion of the human being that he invariably follows brainless or uninhibited individuals unquestioningly. If, in the course of history, irresponsible men have sometimes managed to induce the masses to follow them, their success was certainly not attributable to their defects, but to their talents.

Other phenomena, by contrast, may well permit of comparison. There is undoubtedly food for thought in the fact that in many species of animals the male's sexual urge is positively correlated with aggressive behavior and negatively correlated with fear, whereas the exact opposite applies to the female. Much the same holds good in the case of human beings. In men, a mood of aggression intensifies sexual appetency, whereas fear diminishes it. In women, aggression diminishes sexual preparedness, whereas fear can intensify it. This may be a genuine relationship (in the sense of a homology) or a parallel development (in the sense of a convergence). In either case, it is a noteworthy functional relationship which probably came into being as a result of similar preconditions.

Another instructive parallel is provided by the infantilisms which occur between sexual partners. It is a widespread phenomenon among mammals and birds that the male activates the female's brood-tending instinct in order to approach her and break down her individual barrier. In practice, this means that the male goes through various behavior patterns peculiar to the young of the species, thereby eliciting suitably friendly reactions from the female and facilitating sexual advances. Females, in their turn, activate the protective instinct of the male in order to reinforce bond formation. Analogous procedures can be observed in human couples. Here, too, there is a resort to words and gestures usually employed toward infants. Fondling the other party, soothing him or her with caresses, tending the skin, feeding, the bestowal of childish pet names—all these derive from the behavioral repertory of brood tending and represent, in man's case too, a roundabout way of overcoming a partner's inhibitions by means of entirely different instinctive actions.

One form of animal behavior from which vital information can be gleaned is rooted in the aggressive urge. This is widespread in the animal kingdom and manifests itself in extremely hostile and aggressive behavior toward members of the same species. In his book *On Aggression,* Lorenz gives a detailed account of how this instinct, which is so evidently directed against fellow members of a species, succeeded in asserting itself; of its selective value; and the extent to which it does, ultimately, benefit the species—a subject to which we shall return later. Lorenz lists the aggressive urge, together with those of feeding, procreation, and flight, as one of the four most important human instincts and takes the view that it developed with particular intensity during the early phase of our evolution. This instinct has lost much of its significance in the modern world, with its legal guarantees of security. Indeed, it has become a disadvantage to us because, in a well-ordered society, we lack the opportunity to work it off. This manifests itself in sporadic moods of aggression or irritability which originate within us and are not occasioned by our environment.

If a pair of cichlids are isolated in an aquarium from other members of their species, the male's aggressive urge turns against the female because there are no other males to attack. This may even result in the male's killing the female. If another male is placed in the aquarium, even behind a sheet of glass, the male will violently attack its fellow male and turn into an amicable mate. Cichlids are certainly not to be compared with human beings, but the functional relationship cannot be ignored.

If human beings living at close quarters—whether in the marital home, a military camp, or elsewhere—cannot work off their aggression on something outside, they will turn on their partners or companions.

Can our behavior be improved by an awareness of this state of affairs? Obviously it can. But a mood of irritation cannot be entirely suppressed by the intellect because anger is an instinctive and uncontrollable emotion. What we can attain by an exercise of intellect is the ability not to overrate ourselves in such situations nor take ourselves too seriously.

Similarly, knowledge of animal behavior can help the human being to a better understanding of himself in other respects as well.

PART II

Human Behavior

7

A Voyage of Self-Exploration

To what extent is human behavior determined or influenced by heredity, and how free are human beings in their actions and reactions? Training our cameras on unsuspecting people from hidden vantage points, we searched for something which lay beyond the scope of their "free will." Studying the movements of Chinese, Europeans, American Indians, Hamites, Negroes, Polynesians, Lapps, and others, we sought evidence of something universal and powerful which influences human life counter to the will of the individual. We checked to see if there are behavioral attributes which—whether among black, yellow, or white, rich or poor, educated or uneducated—influence individual actions and so help to determine the course of life. Finally, we explored ourselves.

From the technical point of view, taking close-ups unobserved was particularly difficult because of a human reaction which is probably innate. Being a visual creature, man prefaces every hostile act with a stare. This, presumably, is why the person staring becomes a key stimulus which induces heightened alertness in the person stared at. The lens of a camera bears a resemblance to the human eye, as we were forcibly reminded by a five-year-old Pygmy boy. No sooner had he noticed that I was aiming the camera at him than he instinctively ducked, much as animals do. A few weeks later we recorded almost the same reflex movement in a jackal. With people who are aware of the significance of the camera, psychological factors play a part as well. Many primitive tribesmen believe that someone who acquires part of their person—be it only their likeness—gains a hold over them, but many civilized people show equal annoyance when they notice that they are being photographed because they regard it as an infringement of their privacy.

We solved this problem by equipping the camera with a mirror which enabled me to take films at right angles to the direction in which it was facing. We thus aimed the camera as required, often standing for hours in front of trees, flowers, or houses and observing them with unflagging interest until people gradually became accustomed to us. Life resumed its normal course, and we were even able to film people in our immediate vicinity without their knowledge.

Inquisitive children proved a universal hazard. Anxious not to get in the way, they ranged themselves on either side of the camera and thus obstructed the camera's true line. It also required a great deal of practice to follow moving objects with the mirror tube. Thanks to the reflex effect and transverse camera angle, each camera movement produced a different displacement of the image. The most difficult subject in this respect was the ritual hand movements performed by Hindus bathing in the Ganges.

Ethnologists tend to make things much easier for themselves. They ask a suitable person to perform the appropriate movements in front of the camera, superimpose them on a fitting background, and then repeat the scene as often as it suits them. For purposes of behavioral research, however, such films are worthless. As soon as someone knows that he is being filmed, he ceases to behave naturally. The difference between a genuine and a contrived sequence of movements is far greater than one might suppose, even in the case of dances, which are normally intended for an audience in the first place. To test this, we have first filmed a sequence unobserved and then asked the same person to perform it again in front of the camera. It is astonishing how much fluency and grace a performance loses in the process. Movements executed in an awareness of being filmed take on quite another aspect. If cultural films on the subject of craftsmanship tend to be extremely boring, this is probably because they are contrived. There is almost always something enthralling about the real thing.

Our films yielded many results which we failed to detect until later. Spectators watching accelerated sequences often noticed phenomena which had not occurred to us while shooting. In Venice, for example, I stationed myself on the outer gallery of St. Mark's Cathedral and filmed the patterns of movement made by pedestrians streaming across St. Mark's Square. When the film was shown, one of the audience pointed out that many people did not cross the square by the shortest route (*i.e.,* diagonally) but steered first for a lamppost which was somewhat out of the direct line and then for another before making the complete crossing. This drew our attention to an interesting phenomenon of orientation.

Film shot in a temple at Banaras also yielded unforeseen results. The pilgrims, who entered in batches, touched the rear wall of the temple with raised hands and forehead, and when one pilgrim turned in the course of his obeisance, those following him turned likewise. If a pilgrim then came who did not turn, those immediately following him likewise failed to turn. This was a good illustration of how one human being can influence others by example. We recorded similar occurrences elsewhere. Only the sight of hundreds of people performing the same maneuver in quick succession brings home the extent to which one man's behavior can influence that of his fellows.

On the steps of a church in Rio we found a beggar. Since Eibl took a special interest in begging movements, we set up the camera some distance away, focused it on the man by mirror, and left the camera to run. Instead of begging, however, our subject gradually succumbed to sleep. When speeded up, the film showed how he wrestled with the urge to doze. His head first sank, then jerked upright, in a very definite rhythmical pattern. Within the context of our bodily functions, the urge to sleep acts as a safety valve and prevents sensitive brain cells from being damaged by excessive strain. This sequence made it possible to follow the gradual self-assertion of the urge.

My first ethological discovery was attributable to a film which we made in a remote village on Sawaii, one of the West Samoan islands, where my wife and I were lodging in the headman's house. Since the houses there—known as *fales*—have no walls, only posts, we could easily watch what was going on in the houses around us. Unobserved, we filmed scenes from daily life, including the manner in which people ate their meals. It struck me later that people look around repeatedly while eating, especially if alone. Their eyes glance up abruptly and dart from side to side. This procedure has long been known in animals, being a hereditary coordination referred to as scenting. The risk of being surprised by a predator is, after all, particularly great at feeding time. As our subsequent visual and photographic observations in various parts of the world showed, this hereditarily determined movement has survived in man as well and may be observed in any restaurant. Although we have long ceased to be in danger of attack by predators, we continue —quite unwittingly—to perform these movements with our eyes.

We were able to identify the same procedure among African elephants living in the wild. When the animals drink, they periodically raise their heads and swivel them from side to side. In man, scenting is normally too rapid to attract attention, whereas in elephants it is so slow that it becomes apparent only when speeded up. Varying the speed of a film makes it possible to observe animals, too, from a new and different standpoint. This shows up particularly well in comparative films of animals living in the wild and in captivity. The condition of animals kept in zoos, however well run, becomes horrifyingly apparent in speeded-up films. In elephants, the normal motor rhythm is completely disrupted and permeated with stereotypes. One rhinoceros filmed by us returned again and again to the same post and rubbed its horn in precisely the same manner. Pine martens hopped repeatedly to the corner of their cages in an equally stereotyped way. Bears shuttled back and forth between the same boundary lines with machinelike regularity, hundreds and thousands of times.

We discovered an interesting parallel in man. From the roof of the Vienna Opera I filmed a news vendor whose beat was in front of a projecting section of wall on the other side of the street. At ten times the actual speed, my film showed that the man shuttled to and fro as if between two invisible boundary lines. He faced the street, where his customers were streaming past, but always kept to exactly the same boundaries. For experimental purposes I filmed him again six months later, but the boundaries had not changed. This, too, was an instance where stereotyping had developed into a form of imprisonment.

We were particularly eager to compare the motor rhythms of factory workers operating machines. The same task can often be performed in a number of ways, and it is important, both to the firm and its employees, to find out how a particular operation can be carried out most speedily and with the least possible exertion. It is also instructive to compare workers who are new to a machine with those who have been operating it for years. Such comparisons show how the whole movement is integrated; they also reveal points at which the flow of movement is interrupted. Just as a rock obstructs the natural course of a stream, so factors obstructive to the operation as a whole become visible in films which have been greatly accelerated.

The documentation of human facial movements requires considerable patience. Working among various races, we strove to make unobserved recordings of all the moods and emotions which an actor deliberately conveys to an audience—rage, alarm, expectancy, jealousy, amazement, suspicion, disgust, arrogance, fear, derision, and so on. We crouched in the dirty backyards of American Indian houses, posted ourselves near members of the international set in French luxury hotels, stationed our camera in the midst of hundreds of bawling, singing visitors to the beer tents of the Munich *Oktoberfest,* captured the animated faces of traders and hagglers in street markets. If we saw a quarrel, we tried to edge closer; if we caught sight of people engaged in intimate conversation, we crept up on them with a telephoto lens. Children's faces sometimes betrayed an alternation of emotions quicker than the sequences in a newsreel, and the network of lines in a leathery old face conveyed the distillation of a long span of existence. Whatever the face, we waited patiently to see what would occur in it and tried to gather, from the prevailing situation, what was going on inside its owner.

Here again, chance came to our aid. In Samoa, a pretty young girl watched me apparently filming the deserted sea and became increasingly annoyed that I continued to scan the distant horizon instead of looking at her. She compressed her lips, angrily drove her clenched fist into her open palm, and grew more and more restive. We never succeeded in recording a clearer manifestation of resentment and impatience. In the market at Pisac in the Peruvian highlands, Eibl noticed an Indian woman who had lost her child in the crowd. With the greatest difficulty, I managed to focus my mirror on her face through a sea of bobbing heads and so obtained a unique record of profound consternation and anxiety. A girl whom I filmed on the promenade at Nice was conversing with an elderly man who was evidently paying court to her. She listened to him with a smile, then abruptly drew a veil over her features. She inclined her pretty head, narrowed her eyes, slowly opened her mouth—and gave a hearty yawn. We recorded something similar while filming chimpanzees living in the wild at Jane Goodall's installation at Lake Tanganyika. I had just focused the camera on a placidly seated chimpanzee matron and started filming when she, too, opened her mouth—considerably wider than my first subject—and gave an equally hearty yawn.

We were able in many cases to provoke facial expressions artificially. For instance, Eibl was extremely anxious to record a human being baring his canines in anger. An opportunity presented itself in a lonely district in Kenya, where we came across two Karamojo warriors who badgered us for money. As soon as I had hastily set up the camera and trained the mirror correctly, Eibl gave one of them the smallest coin we possessed. The man interpreted this as an insult and flew into a rage. He expressed his opinion of us forcibly in unintelligible dialect, clearly revealing his canines in the process. Eibl put the coin back in his pocket while I rewound the camera. Then he fished out the same coin and proffered it a second time. It should be remembered that both men had spears in their hands and that there was nobody else for miles around. I managed to save the situation by producing a ten-shilling note from my pocket and handing it over. We had achieved our object. The two men departed in high dudgeon, but their canines were preserved for posterity.

Eibl was also interested in obtaining as many pictures as

possible of the human "eye greeting"—a slight widening of the eyes coupled with a raising of the brows, principally employed in flirtation. This signal—very probably another hereditary coordination—proved to be a more entertaining subject. We trained the mirror on various specimens of femininity, and while one of us did the filming, the other eyed them as seductively as he could—though without using the signal in question. Many of the ladies simply stared at us in surprise, but many others reacted as required.

We also had good results in Japan with a box containing a toy snake which sprang out when the lid was unscrewed. This time Eibl did the filming while I joined strangers on park benches. I smiled amiably at my victim, held out the box, unscrewed it, and the snake popped out. We obtained some striking records of the transition from polite inquiry to shock and bewilderment. At Luxor, in the Valley of the Kings, street vendors swarm over arriving tourists like locusts and try to sell them chains, scarabs, and other souvenirs. Here again we used artificial means to get what we wanted in the way of a performance. I set up the camera on one of the bare hills overlooking the road and, using a telephoto lens, filmed my wife as she drove up in the car and climbed out. Two souvenir sellers instantly hurled themselves at her, and all she had to do was stand there with an air of indecision. The result was a filmed record of all the gestures that both men had at their command.

We conducted one particular experiment in the solution of conflict situations in various towns, mostly from hotel windows. We set up the camera so that it could not be seen from below, trained it on a footpath or pavement, and started shooting. Meanwhile, one of us had unobtrusively visited the spot, drawn a circle on the ground with chalk, placed a large bank note in the center, weighed it down with a stone, and left.

It was astonishing how many people passed such a bait without noticing it. Those that did so exhibited a variety of reactions. In Nairobi we filmed a man who stood rooted to the spot (it was a pound note), then swiftly picked up his find and walked on, then halted, hurried back, and replaced the money in the circle. Another man performed a 90-degree turn and vanished across some fields. On a busy pavement, countless pedestrians streamed past the spot without pausing, though most of them avoided the circle. Finally, one man paused and stared at the bank note. Another followed suit, and within minutes a circle had formed. Our accelerated film showed how the throng became denser and more animated until one particular individual came to the fore. He talked vehemently—the circle thinned—then suddenly he picked up the note. The crowd clustered around him, and the whole gaggle of humanity, with the courageous individual in its midst, surged off.

Back home we sat in front of the viewer, splicing various sequences together and comparing them for points of difference and correspondence. Once flesh-and-blood, the people we had filmed were transformed into marionettes, and we asked ourselves who or what manipulated the strings which controlled their individual movements. Was it their "free will"? Was it upbringing and education? Or was it cerebral mechanisms which are common to people the world over?

8

Man and Curiosity

THE observation of man would present a visitor from outer space with many problems. Let us imagine that an invisible spaceship has landed on a snowcapped peak in the Alps, and that its occupants are gazing down on a winter resort in the valley. They are confronted by the sight of human beings trudging or riding up the white slopes and then gliding downhill with monotonous regularity. Our unseen visitors may be forgiven for pondering on the significance of such actions.

The earth creatures cannot be looking for food—that would seem obvious. There is nothing edible on the slopes, only snow and rock, so the purpose of all this bustle and activity is obscure. Animals sometimes gather at a preordained spot for mating purposes, but can this apply here? Although the figures hurrying up and down the slopes are moving in pairs or groups, their movements seem to betoken a different intention. But what intention? What do they gain by such an expenditure of energy?

Such were the questions suggested to us by films which we had shot in Sankt Christoph am Arlberg and projected at ten times the actual speed. We have grown so accustomed to the sight of sporting activities at normal speed that they seldom impress us as a specifically human peculiarity. As everyone knows, part of their *raison d'être* is the product of rational deliberation on the part of the sportsman, who desires to develop his physique and stay healthy. There are also prizes to be won and other people to be impressed, but that does not exhaust the list of motives. What underlies such activities is something else, something instinctive: a need to acquire new abilities, to try out new aptitudes—an urge to step outside the confines of everyday life, a desire for change and novelty.

Another scene: the Acropolis at Athens. Here again we filmed visitors' comings and goings and projected them at ten times the actual speed, and here again our film gave us food for thought. The visitor from outer space would again be puzzled by the expenditure of energy. People had traveled long distances—even crossed oceans—to see something which was of no practical benefit to them. Why? There is an instinctive element in tourism too: a yearning to abandon one's normal habitat, break the bounds of one's accustomed sphere, and acquire new impressions—a desire for change and novelty.

On the beach at Nice I filmed a young man who was sitting reading the paper surrounded by bathers. Again accelerated projection afforded some entirely new insights. The young man plowed through his paper, picked up another, plowed through that one, picked up a third, and when he had finished it, reached for the first again. When reading newspapers and books, we have long ceased to be aware that we are ingesting information that has virtually no meaning for us. Conversations which we filmed all over the world left the same impression. They had ceased to be an exchange of relevant information and, in many cases, had become mere chatter. Novelty is a source of pleasure to us. That is one essential reason why we are attracted by public functions and lured by theater, cinema, and the television screen. We yearn for variety. We want to step outside the cramped confines of daily life, at least in our imagination. Our senses thirst for new impressions. We are animated by an urge, a craving, for novelty—in a word, by curiosity.

Is this a special characteristic which distinguishes us from animals? Yes, but only in part. Many animals display similar instinctive behavior, though usually only until they attain sexual maturity.

As we have already mentioned, all creatures which acquire part of their behavior by learning possess an innate urge to grapple actively with their environment. The young rat, the young crow, the young lion—all try out their entire behavior repertory in play. They investigate the nature of the material objects which compose their environment, twist and turn them, try all kinds of maneuvers with them, and thereby acquire the experience necessary to learning by practice. Separate hereditary coordinations, often consisting of very brief motor sequences, are thus welded together into longer concatenations of successful behavior.

Another noteworthy factor is, for instance, that the urge to play takes longer to satisfy than other urges. The appetency to play remains operative far longer than other appetencies, which soon subside when indulged. Moreover, this fully accords with the biological purpose of the procedure. Only by repeated practice and testing can an animal gain the sureness of touch and movement so essential to its continued existence.

That the goal of this instinctive behavior is novelty for its own sake emerges from observations made by Lorenz. An inquisitively inclined creature will not be distracted from the investigation of objects still unknown to it, even by familiar tidbits. Even when the creature is trying out the motor patterns of eating—in other words, playing at eating—it will give a strange practice object priority over a known delicacy. To quote Lorenz: "Anthropomorphically speaking, the creature does not want to eat; it wants to 'know' everything there is, 'theoretically,' to eat within its particular habitat."

Analogous instinctive behavior is clearly discernible in the young human being. In general, the mother represents the first object of its curiosity and play behavior. The child feels and explores her face, thereby gaining its first conception of space. As soon as it can crawl, it starts to explore its immediate environment. It feels objects, conveys them to its mouth, turns them over, and thus gains experience of their properties. Herein lies the great importance to a child of the toy, which with primitive children often consists of no more than a stone or twig. By handling such things the child learns how objects can be moved and how they behave when brought into contact with each other. It learns the relationship between cause and effect and, at the same time, the potentialities of its body and hands.

Curiosity and play are certainly not identical in our linguistic usage, yet it is highly probable that both phenomena have a common root. The difference lies merely in the fact that curiosity leads to exploration and mastery of one's environment, whereas play leads to exploration and mastery of new capabilities. In the first instance the prime object is information; in the second the construction of motor patterns. There is, however, a similar instinctive striving for novelty in both instances. Either this is a case where two different urges are very similar in effect, or, alternatively, the striving for new knowledge and the striving for new ability—the first relating to sensation and the second to movement—are operated by the same motor.

The curiosity instinct conflicts with that of fear. Curiosity impels, fear restrains. Many of our slow-motion films of children illustrated the resulting conflict behavior. They showed, on the one hand, how children are tempted and challenged by their unfamiliar environment, and, on the other, how an inner voice warns them to approach the unfamiliar with caution and be tentative in taking new steps.

Parental protection is of decisive importance here. If a living creature is not "complete" at birth and must first acquire vital and indispensable skills, protection is a prerequisite of survival. Parents, therefore, in the course of evolution, parallel with the degeneration of instinctive control and the development of the ability to learn, must have evolved an instinct for the preservation of their young. The one would have been quite impossible without the other. The butterfly pays no heed to the caterpillars that emerge from its eggs, once it has laid them. These come into the world complete, however, and can survive without care and protection thanks to behavior which is innate in them. The learner, on the other hand, is dependent upon the laborious process of exploration and practice, and in this helpless state it derives protection both from its parents' brood-tending instinct and from its own fear. Thus the degeneration of one set of instincts rendered it necessary to develop and strengthen other instincts.

Accelerated films provided us with a clear illustration of how the behavior of children and parents is mutually attuned. Mother and child are linked as though by an invisible elastic band. As soon as the child leaves her side, the mother reacts with anxiety—indeed, she reacts almost constantly to the child even when otherwise occupied. Little by little, the child ventures farther from her, explores the world around it, tests its abilities, plays with this object or that. On beaches and in parks we recorded how children use parents as aids to practice. They clamber around on them, engage in trials of strength with them, and elicit the same reactions with monotonous frequency —and their parents not only indulge but positively encourage them. Similar behavior was observable in baboons which we filmed under similar circumstances.

One important aspect of exploration consists in the ability to stand aloof from the current object of interest. The human baby does not at first possess this ability. Having once grasped an object, it conveys it to its mouth and can only break this rigid sequence of actions with difficulty. As the child grows older, one can see it remove the object from its mouth, examine it, convey it to its mouth again, and then, perhaps, discard it or grasp it with the other hand or throw it away—and so on. Only the most intelligent learners (*e.g.*, dogs and monkeys) show the same ability to dissociate themselves from an object and explore it from another angle by trying a new line of approach.

One very characteristic feature of active play is the persistence with which new and successful actions are reiterated. Once a child finds out how to build a tower of bricks and knock it down, it will repeat the process. Once it has summoned the courage to slide down a chute, it will do it again and again. Every new ability resembles a victory, a pleasurable accretion of power. Step by step, the child conquers its environment and brings more and more objects within its sphere of influence. Precisely the same applies to the higher learning animals. A young badger reared by Eibl, which had discovered how to turn somersaults in the course of play, repeated the trick over and over again. Every series of movements which is in any way purposive is ingrained by repetition so that the commands in the brain become firmly knit. Acquired coordinations created in this way remain at the animal's disposal; from now on, it keeps them in stock.

The use of surrogates, or substitutes, is also interesting. A young lion treats its brothers and sisters as if they were prey, and so practices preying behavior. A young polecat reared indoors by Eibl occupied a wastepaper basket and defended it in exactly the same way as the adult animal defends its nest. To the child, ball and sandbox are ideal substitutes, the ball for practicing chasing, catching, and grasping; the sand for testing the creative ability of hands—and mind.

Experimental play develops into constructive play. The tendency to dismember things—a procedure which helps augment knowledge of material objects—can also be observed in birds and the higher mammals. The assembling of objects, on the other hand, is peculiar to children and young monkeys. Lorenz writes:

> It is quite astonishing what the young of the lower apes, *e.g.*, the Capuchin (*Cebus*), manage to achieve during such games in the way of superimposition and insertion of objects, employment of leverage effects, and the like. Their experiments, which are intensive and betray a businesslike concentration on the matter in hand, create an almost human impression.

Is human curiosity and play behavior really free to take any direction, or is the impulse to acquire information and aptitudes subject to definite guidelines? Are the things that a child learns during its experimental games governed by some system of herditarily fixed priorities?

With animals there is no doubt that games are influenced by learning dispositions. With herbivores, to whom aggressive action is less important than escape from predators, flight games predominate. With predators, hunting and fighting games take precedence. When, with children, we note that girls incline toward dolls while boys favor climbing (fruit seeking) and playing with weapons (hunting), we are acknowledging a division of interests which is obviously influenced by heredity. Playing house is typical of young human beings—boys and girls alike. To the physically vulnerable human being, the creation of a suitable place of refuge is of special importance, so it is not surprising that we developed a play preference in this dierction.

Of course, games are also strongly influenced by adult activities and cultural traditions. "Fashions," which determine the course of individual games, have been demonstrated in monkeys and other animals. The imitative urge, which is strongly developed in many learners, plays an equally important role in young human beings. It impels them to adopt motor patterns observed in their parents. Even the so-called spells of defiance, to which we shall return later, may possibly derive from hereditarily fixed learning dispositions. What the child is learning here—also in play, although it seems entirely serious—is how to pit its own will against that of its parents. The growing creature is developing individuality and independence, the ability to assess alternatives and form decisions, which is so important to its continued existence.

There is, however, a substantial difference between animal and human being in this respect. Inquisitive behavior wanes or disappears completely in all learners after sexual maturity. This is not the case with human beings, who retain most of their youthful curiosity until old age. We remain interested in novelty and the possibility of change. As the German sociologist Gehlen put it, the human being remains "open to the world."

Once a learner—a wolf or lion, for example—attains maturity, it has acquired all the aptitudes important to survival and displays no impulse to acquire more. The animals is, as it were, embedded in a particular environment and mode of existence and shows no desire to break bounds. Men are different in this respect. Proceeding from our ancestors' original tropical habitat, we populated the entire globe, tried our luck virtually everywhere, and when conditions were unsatisfactory, created an artificial environment suitable to our needs. This development would certainly have been impossible had it not been for our superior intelligence, yet our persistent inquisitive urge must surely have made a substantial contribution. This was the motor which impelled us to take an interest in novelty. This was what invested us with the basic readiness to grapple with very changed circumstances and master them in a new way.

The urge to defy difficulty or danger finds particular expression in sporting activities. Many people gamble with their lives when climbing, diving, or winter sporting. A similar tendency is apparent in risky business ventures and in scientific research. The scientist has always been an inquisitive, indeed, playful character. Most discoveries and inventions have occurred because of the pronounced streak of curiosity to be found in many individuals, not as the result of a rational and objective striving for personal gain. It is not merely because of our intellect that man's evolution has been marked by an endeavor to push back frontiers and cross them, that new and often fantastic schemes and ideas have sprung up with each succeeding generation, that we are pressing forward into space. No, this intellect of ours is controlled by an instinctive peculiarity which resides within us, by a force which decisively influences and guides our will.

It is characteristic of the inquisitive urge that it makes itself felt with particular force when no other instinctive pressure exists, in other words, when other impulses have waned. This applies to all learners, including man. As Schiller put it: "The animal works when a deficiency is the mainspring of its activity and plays when the mainspring is an abundance of strength." As long as his actions are governed, say, by fear, hunger, or sexual desire, man is not inquisitive either. He does not play or playfully embark upon new ventures. Only when he is without other appetencies does he become venturesome and willful. It is then that he feels an urge to abandon the normal pattern of existence, whatever the alternative. It is then that the Dionysiac, the daring and truly human element in man, comes to the fore.

Experiments with songbirds have shown that they produce their most varied and beautiful songs outside their procreative period rather than during it. That is when they "compose," as the bird lover describes it. Again, chimpanzees to which Morris gave brushes, paints, and canvas produced paintings during their relaxed period, which disclosed a basic aesthetic sense of symmetry and balance. These and similar observations make it reasonable to assume that our play and curiosity impulse is responsible not only for discovery, exploration, and innovation, but also, in large measure, for promoting our artistic development.

In his treatise on *Whole and Part in the Animal and Human Community,* Lorenz set forth the main features of inquisitive behavior—in fact, the term *Neugierwesen,* or "curiosity creature," stems from him. His point of departure was the distinction between specialized and nonspecialized creatures. The specialists are fitted for a very specific way of life in which they wield superiority over all rivals, whereas the nonspecialists have the advantage of being adaptable and, thus, independent of one particular environmental situation. Although their competitive ability may thus be less in individual instances, they are, by way of compensation, less vulnerable to the danger of changes in environment. Thanks to their learning capacity, they can conform to such changes. All curiosity creatures are thoroughgoing nonspecialists. Their behavior patterns are hereditarily fixed to only a small degree, and their innate releasing mechanisms (IRM's) generally respond to widespread—and thus characteristic deficient—key stimuli. They treat everything new "as if it were of supreme biological importance to them" and so "unerringly discover, in the most varied and extreme environments, every factor which can contribute to the preservation of their life." Man is the most advanced of all curiosity creatures. In him, curiosity and readiness to learn persist into old age; in him, this instinctive behavior is carried to the extreme.

In this context, Lorenz described man as a "specialist in nonspecialization." Like Gehlen, he sees "one of the constituent characteristics of man—indeed, perhaps the most important of them—in his perpetually inquisitive and exploratory confrontation with the world of material objects; in his specifically human tendency actively to improve his own environment." We shall return more than once to the practical form taken by such improvements.

How did it actually come about, this remarkable difference between us and the learners related to us? How is it that this instinct is not extinguished in us at sexual maturity? Lorenz ascribes this to two phenomena. Both are controversial, but we shall cite them just the same.

As Bolk expounded in 1926, man has a number of "persisting youthful characteristics." He listed them as the combination of hairless body and hairy head; the superimposition of cranium upon facial structure; the almost 90-degree relationship of the base of the skull to the spine (together with the correspondingly advanced position of the occipital cavity); a heavy brain (heavy in relation to body weight); various structural features of the female sex organs; the pigmentation of the skin; and others besides. These peculiarities are also found—a remarkable parallel—in the early stages of development of anthropoid apes. Ape embryos are also hairless (except for the head) and display all the other special features enumerated above. Thus man is reminiscent of the fetus of the anthropoid ape. In this connection, Bolk spoke of a fetalization of man—a theory which not only attracted attention but, inevitably, aroused a great deal of antipathy as well. To many people, the notion that we are descended from apes was bad enough; the idea that we might, as it were, represent an embryonic stage in the development of the anthropoid ape struck them as grotesque.

Examples of inhibited development are not rare in the animal world. Some creatures—crabs and Diptera and salamanders come to mind—attain sexual maturity at a relatively early stage of development and do not, therefore, complete the rest of a developmental cycle which can still be clearly followed in related species. The zoologist refers to this phenomenon as neoteny. The classic example of this is the axolotl, a batrachian reptile in which the phenomenon can be traced to this day. In its larval state this creature has gills and lives in water. Later it loses its gills and develops into a land-dwelling salamander. In many cases, the larvae attain sexual maturity. These specimens retain their gills and remain aquatic creatures. Where such a process has become hereditary, it has led, in the course of evolution, to the development of many new species.

Lorenz, referring to other symptoms of inhibited development listed by Bolk, described man's persistently inquisitive behavior as an example of neoteny. He also accounted for the occurrence of human neoteny by construing it as a possible effect of domestication. Examples of neoteny had earlier been demonstrated in domestic animals on the basis of various physical characteristics. Proceeding further, Lorenz found symptoms

My technique for photographing people unobserved: A dummy complete with prism is mounted in front of the lens so that I appear to be aiming in another direction. This enables me to take close-ups of people without their knowledge. Depicted are rickshaw coolies in Hong Kong, but hardly anyone spotted the trick, even in Europe.

One example of an innate mode of behavior (fixed-action pattern) in man is yawning. The biological significance of this expressive movement lies in its power to transmit mood. All social animals benefit if the life rhythm of group members—including their sleeping habits—is synchronized. Yawning is infectious, *i.e.,* it transmits a sense of fatigue.

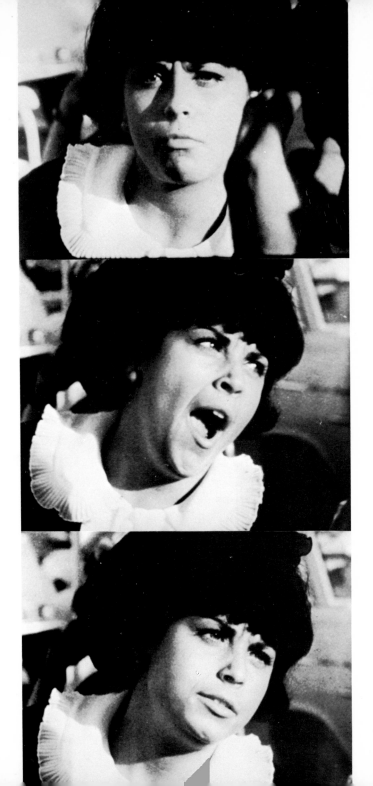

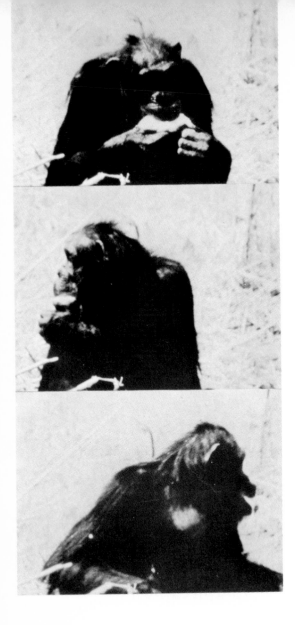

Another fixed-action pattern peculiar to man and most of the higher vertebrates is automatically glancing around during a meal. Civilized man has long ceased to be in danger of surprise attack by predators while eating, yet this involuntary movement persists in us, too. After every third or fourth bite the eyes dart momentarily from side to side.

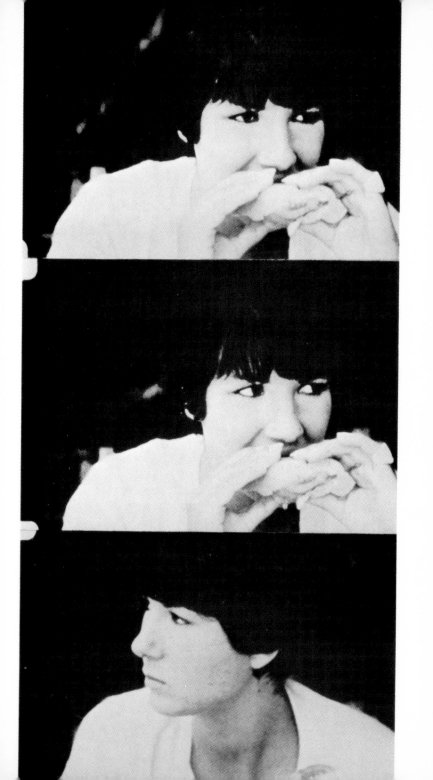

Yet another fixed-action pattern is the human smile, which innately allays aggressive tendencies in other human beings, discloses a readiness to make contact, and arouses goodwill. The smile of a baby when suckled produces a strong reaction in the mother; reinforces her bond with the child—her "mother love." As the child develops, it learns to employ this facial signal at need, in order to secure goodwill or the fulfillment of a wish.

The basic movements of flirting are also innate in the human being and common to women the world over. These consist in a smile of provocation and invitation followed by a "bashful" lowering of the eyes, a turning away, withdrawal, and apparent tendency toward flight. Visual contact is then resumed, and the ambivalent motor sequence may be repeated. (Unobserved slow-motion film of a Turkana tribeswoman flirting. Six seconds elapsed between the first and fourth frames.)

Another fixed-action pattern (innate sequence of movements), which we covertly filmed in slow motion in various parts of the world, is the "ocular greeting." The smile is coupled with an abrupt arching of the eyebrows. The sequence reproduced here, which was filmed by Eibl-Eibesfeldt, illustrates this facial signal of goodwill in a native whose tribe had first come into contact with white men only two years before. Quite obviously, it could not have been acquired by imitation of other races.

The same facial signal in a Frenchwoman and (overleaf) a Samoan. The whole process was very rapid. In all three cases the eyebrows were raised for only .16 second. Some leading American psychologists still support the erroneous view that everything—including facial expression—is acquired by learning and imitation. Consequently, they also claim that anything can be instilled into man by education. Ethological research—and our films—refute this beyond all reasonable doubt.

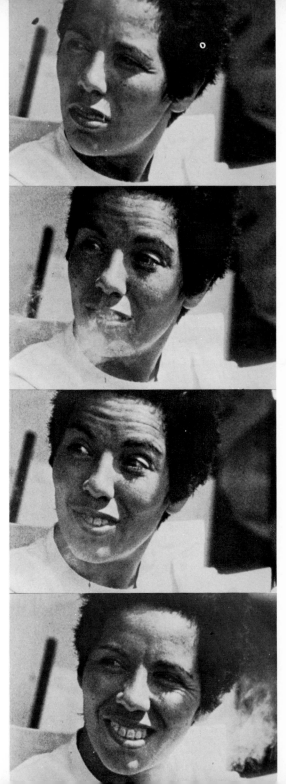

Unobserved photographs of a South American Indian woman who had lost her child in a crowd. The expressive movements indicating help-lessness, sorrow, and despair are likewise identical all over the world: They are innate. An actor would find it hard to reproduce such expressions with the same power of conviction.

Dismay at the receipt of bad news, portrayed by a Japanese actress. The actor seeks to emphasize typical features and transmit "supernormal stimuli": a tense facial expression, downward-curving lips, a furrowed brow, a suggestion of weeping and suppressed sobs.

Chinese woman in a fury: movements conveying an intention to bite and strike. *Opposite:* Ritualized fury in the classical Japanese theater. The baring of the eyeteeth is a minatory signal inherited from our animal forebears, whose canines were more strongly developed. The erstwhile weapon has regressed, but the fixed-action pattern survives.

Man extended his body by means of "artificial organs"—initially weapons, clothes, articles of jewelry, tools, etc. This Turkana warrior from northern Kenya wears an unusual artificial organ on his belt: It functions during the day as a stool, at night as a headrest designed to preserve his elaborate hairstyle intact.

of neoteny in their behavior as well. Man has shielded himself against natural selection in much the same way as he protects his domestic animals from natural threats, and Lorenz had already pointed to other human peculiarities which he estimated to be the outcome of this self-domestication. On the strength of such considerations, he advanced the theory that man's persistently inquisitive behavior is a form of neoteny which, in turn, is a consequence of self-domestication.

The peculiarity of our inquisitive behavior emerged only gradually in the course of evolutionary history. Our ancestors had been using tools for a long time before they began to detach themselves from their natural surroundings and proceed to overcome nature itself, deliberately modify their existence and shape it artificially. Each innovation led to a new habit, a new tradition. Passed on during the process of rearing, these usually rigid behavior patterns themselves became antitheses of change. Indeed, they sometimes became a self-made barrier which further inquisitive behavior had to strive to surmount.

In the remote village of El Molo beside Lake Rudolf in Kenya we covertly filmed children at play building "houses" with reeds and scraps of cloth. The behavior pattern discernible in our film showed how the children worked together and how they modeled their houses on the local kraal. Finally, they ran off and became engrossed in some other game. We were on the point of packing up when a little girl appeared. She stood in front of one of the ramshackle edifices and contemplated it thoughtfully. Then, with sudden resolution, she walked up to it, dismantled it, and tried to convert the rags that had served as a roof into a skirt and shawl. Commonplace as it may appear, this little incident contains the essence of what human evolution has had to contend with, always and everywhere. Before something new can be tried or created, often something already in existence has to be destroyed. This applies to small things as to large and has frequently been the cause of war and revolution.

However, we are not the only creatures to be faced with this vexing problem. Practically all advanced organic development, from the first molecular complexes to exhibit life down to mammals and human beings, has been confronted by it.

"Without rigid structures," writes Lorenz, "no organic system of an advanced level of integration is possible, but the structures of the existing system must be smashed before another of a still higher level of integration can be attained." Later he adds, "Whether a crab sheds its shell, or a human being exchanges the personality structure of a child for that of an adult, or an obsolete order of human society yields to a new one, evolutionary progress is always and everywhere associated with danger, because the old structure must be dismantled before the new one has attained full operative capacity." Man has always been relatively more exposed to this danger than any other creature. We are, after all, the first and only creatures which can not only adapt but are also capable of fundamentally changing ourselves and our own pattern of existence. Nietzsche called man "the still unestablished animal," and Gehlen, somewhat more accurately, called him "the creature at risk, the creature with an inherent prospect of disaster." The alarming accuracy of the latter description is becoming ever more apparent in today's world with its breakneck technological advances. Never in the course of history has man hesitated to employ all available resources in order to bring about the changes he has in mind. Today, in the nuclear age, this indeed brings us perilously close to the "inherent prospect of disaster."

As man gained mastery over nature, so a fateful conjunction of cause and effect came into being. The more we guaranteed our survival, the more leisure time we gained, and the further we penetrated the zone of relaxation. This zone became a breeding ground for the development of our curiosity drive, which led us on to further experiments, further ideas, further accretions of power. A chimpanzee, Sultan, at the ape station in Tenerife could not at first solve the problem of how to fish a banana into its cage by fitting two sticks together. He continued to experiment with one section or the other until he flew into a rage and gave up. Later, while playing with sticks, he fitted them together by chance. He at once returned to the unsolved task and hooked the banana inside. Having failed to solve the problem under instinctive pressure, he had solved it in the relaxed zone of play. The same must apply to many human discoveries and inventions. Many new ideas are undoubtedly born of necessity and despair, but there is little doubt that man evolves many innovations in the course of leisure-time experimentation.

We tend to regard curiosity as a commonplace and sometimes undesirable characteristic, which certainly is not a human peculiarity. Consideration of the creatures most closely related to us reveals, nevertheless, that it is a phenomenon to which we owe a great deal. Among our animal kin, the instinct which permits them to adapt generally retains its efficacy for only a few years. In man, the drive persists. Our receptiveness to new ideas survives well beyond our sexual prime; our interest in exploring new possibilities endures into old age. Furthermore, our mental powers are often involved in the investigation of the outwardly trivial and meaningless, but this often leads to the discovery of things which are most meaningful. Once such an advance has been made, it usually asserts and establishes itself and enters the realm of custom and tradition. But no sooner has something new come into being than the process of change and disintegration begins all over again. We are curiosity creatures par excellence. We are "creatures at risk," "unestablished animals." We challenge nature even when the odds are against us. We wend our precarious way along a knife edge. We modify ourselves and shed our skin almost unceasingly. And at each such skin shedding we are "in danger."

9

Artificial Organs

EW things seem more natural to human beings than the use of tools. From our earliest childhood onward we are continually picking up and using them. However natural it may appear, let us try to view this activity with different eyes.

Let us start by visualizing how tiny unicellular organisms developed into large multicellular creatures. Most probably this process began when unicellular organisms divided but did not diverge. Instead, a certain number of them remained together and formed a colony. As time went by, individual cells in these cellular colonies began to specialize in certain functions. Some formed a protective skin, others became muscular tissue which enabled the colony to propel itself along, and still others went to make up a supporting skeleton, nerves, and so on. The structural formula was contained in the germ cells whose equally specialized function it was to detach themselves from the colony when it had grown sufficiently and form new colonies. The evolution-promoting institution of bisexuality—the occasional fusion of germ cells—already existed in unicellular organisms and was preserved. Stated very simply, this is the process which, according to current theory, led to the formation of increasingly complicated multicellular organisms. Each such organism is a system for the division of labor. Hundreds and thousands—indeed, millions—of cells go to make up individual organs. They are like factory units designed to fulfill specific functions. Each organ has certain requirements: It demands nutrition, repair, and continuous transportation by the body as a whole. The body has to tend it, protect it, and supply it with energy. Each organ performs certain services but does, from another angle, constitute a burden. Moreover, no living creature has yet managed to slough off temporarily unwanted organs and then graft them onto its body again as required.

Many creatures need their sexual organs, for example, only once a year or once in a lifetime, yet they have to carry them about constantly, nourish, tend, and defend them. Although many organs are of no use to a sleeping animal, they still have to be nourished. Yet in man we are confronted by a creature which can discard organs and exchange them for others. Far from being natural or obvious, this is an enormity from the evolutionary standpoint—an advance laden with unfathomable consequences.

The word "tool" is a misleading one. It is not merely an implement for working upon something, but an extension of our body effected by the artificial addition of organs; an advance to which, to a greater or lesser degree, we owe our civilization.

We tend to suppose that the basis of human progress is our specially developed intellect or intelligence. This is only partly true. Equally important was a second prerequisite, an organ which enabled us to produce artifacts and link them with our bodies: the human hand.

Let us imagine that wolves, lions, or antelopes had developed a brain similar to that of the human being 1,000,000 years ago. How would they be today? Not so very different, simply because a lion's or wolf's paws and an antelope's hoofs are incapable of fashioning artificial organs and harnessing them to the body as a whole. A lion might conceivably be able to guide a pencil with its jaws but could never manufacture one. Once we view things from this angle, our unwelcome kinsfolk, the apes, suddenly assume an entirely different perspective.

Being tree climbers, they developed limbs suitable for climbing. Thus they could reach fruit more easily and escape predators by taking refuge in the branches. They had a secure basis for survival, and they multiplied. Periods of drought ensued.

Trees became sparse, areas of steppe expanded. Then, so contemporary theory holds, the apes were compelled to move from tree to tree by traversing the open ground between them. Because the trees no longer provided adequate nutrition, some species—among them our ancestors—resorted to hunting other animals in the steppe. The apes' stance, which had already been comparatively erect during their arboreal phase, now enabled them to see over the tall grass. They learned how to walk upright on their hind legs, and their prehensile paws were suddenly available for other purposes.

A further concomitant of this process was the enlargement of the brain. In the upright stance, the head is supported by the spinal column. Cells which had hitherto formed the strong dorsal muscles required to carry the head were thus deprived of work. Gradually, these organs became involuted and the skull increased in size. We still do not know exactly how this enlargement came about, but the skull expanded until it eventually reposed balanced above the spinal cord. The brain pan became larger in the process, and the number of ganglion cells housed in that cavity multiplied considerably. The functional capacity of the organ formed by them—the brain—increased as a result. Casts taken from fossil skulls have enabled scientists to trace the development of individual areas of the brain. Increased volume is particularly noticeable in the case of the forebrain—in other words, that part of the brain in which our associative thought processes now take place. Our closest relatives among the anthropoid apes have a cerebral capacity of between 300 and 685 cubic centimeters, whereas our ancestors, the australopithecines, already varied between 450 and 800 cubic centimeters. This figure has risen to between 1,000 and 1,800 cubic centimeters in races of men living today.

The immense time it took for the brain to attain its present efficiency can be gauged from the fact that our ancestors continued to use a very few primitive tools (notably the flint) for 500,000 years. During this time, differentiation occurred in a particular area of the forebrain—the convolution of Broca—to which we owe our power of speech. Primeval men living in hunting communities now acquired the ability to communicate verbally, and this must have hastened the development which was already in progress.

It was still a very long time before man reached the agricultural and cattle-breeding stage, before he learned to manufacture artificial organs such as pot, plow, and cart. Progress really accelerated only in the last 10,000 years—a development which would have been impossible without the prehensile hands inherited from our ape forebears.

Let us take a somewhat closer look at man's artificial organs. Where do their advantages and disadvantages lie?

Their primary advantage is that they do not consist of living cells and thus have no need of constant nourishment. This brings a corresponding saving in the human energy budget. Their second advantage is that they can be discarded or stored when not in use. Consequently, man does not have to carry them about constantly. This effects a further saving of energy. Their third advantage is that they are exchangeable. This makes man the most highly specialized creature in the world. If he holds a spear, he is a hunting specialist; if he grasps an oar, he is a specialist in locomotion; if he operates a loom, he becomes a weaving specialist. It took the multicellular organisms immense periods of time to acquire specialized organs—and remain tied to them—by means of cell differentiation, whereas man succeeded in creating his own specialized organs and harnessing them to his body as required. From the biological aspect, man turned into a quick-change artist of unique skill.

A fourth advantage: Artificial organs could be used by different individuals. A knife may be used first by one person and then, immediately afterward, by another. That is an enormous advantage, especially in a community. In a wolf pack, each individual must produce every organ natural to the wolf, whereas in a human community a single artificial organ such as a scythe or fireplace can be used communally or by different individuals in succession. Colony-building insects had already evolved a similar "rationalization," but on a hereditary basis. Among bees, the queen handles all the egg laying; among termites, specially trained warriors undertake the defense of the nest. Here again the community possesses certain organs, but these are fewer in number and do not have to be developed by the general run of the community. Man, on the other hand, can create these kinds of specialized organs artificially and pass them on from one individual to another. Once again there is a considerable saving in material resources and energy.

The fifth advantage is especially important: The individual need not manufacture the artificial organs he uses. This is what gave rise to the development of the handicrafts and occupations to which we shall return in a later chapter. By specializing in a particular form of manufacture, man can also carry it on better and more rationally. This, too, leads to a saving of energy which is additionally associated with qualitative improvement.

It is worth mentioning a sixth advantage, namely, that the manufacture of an artificial organ need not be underwritten by one individual alone. Several people can share in the costs of such manufacture and can employ the organ communally or in turn, owning it jointly. Hire and sale—equally unthinkable in the case of natural organs—now became possible.

These advantages are, however, balanced by a disadvantage: Artificial organs require protection. Natural organs cannot be stolen. True, one animal may bite a piece off another, but that piece serves it only as nourishment and does not retain its original function. A lizard may bite off an insect's wings, but it cannot use them to fly. An artificial organ, by contrast, can be used equally well by another human being, which is why the problem of property has become so important to human beings. There are numerous theories and accounts of how man came to form communities and evolve various types of social order, and probably such developments did not always follow the same course. What is certain is that they were always governed by the need to protect artificial organs. Man could thus increase his power by creating artificial organs, but these were mortgaged from the very start by the necessity of adequately protecting them.

In the course of the last 6,000 years—and particularly in the last 100 years—our artificial organs have multiplied to a truly gargantuan extent. In the process they have become so remote from our bodies that their connection with it often is scarcely discernible. Moreover, man has always regarded such structures as distinct entities. Because artificial organs are not a part of us, because they are not flesh and blood, because they originated differently from our natural organs and seldom resemble them, we have consigned them to another drawer in our mental filing system. From the biological and evolutionary points of view, this is wrong. They are one and all extensions of our body, and their contributory function can be construed only in this light.

It is obvious that a set of false teeth constitutes an artificial organ because it replaces our natural teeth. A pair of glasses improves an impaired organ instead of replacing a deficient one. Hence, it is a supplementary functional unit which enhances our physical powers and is, in this sense, an artificial organ. Unlike glasses, binoculars are not worn permanently over the eyes; a telescope requires its own support; and the giant telescopes with which we look deep into space are infinitely larger than the astronomers who use them. They are anchored to a particular spot and require an entire building of their own. Thus, an artificial organ may be larger than man himself; it need not be attached to his body; it does not have to be carried about and can, instead, develop into a static contrivance which man employs by approaching it rather than by applying it to his person.

The brain, a natural organ, was also improved in this way. The earliest written tablets, which were found in Mesopotamia, served as aids to human memory. In the course of time, similar clay tablets were additionally used to send messages, thus becoming artificial organs of communication. This development was continued by paper, pen, printing press, typewriter, and so on. A library—yet another large static unit—is also, ultimately, an artificial organ. This example demonstrates that artificial organs may be created by the community as a whole and shared among its individual members. Further instances of communal organs are the postal service, in its capacity as an organized body for the transmission of information; the police and the military, in their capacity as even larger organized bodies set up for man's protection.

Yet another line of development: Hide and fur protect animals from injury on the one hand and cold on the other, so our shoes and clothing represent an artificial improvement of these functions. A still more effective form of protection, though one which ties us to a single spot, is the house or apartment. We rent hotel rooms on a temporary basis; as long as they remain at our disposal, they too serve as artificial organs. Thus, possession of artificial organs may be temporary.

In Kenya Eibl and I filmed Sunjo tribesmen who still tilled their fields with mattocks. The mattock had no need to be manufactured artificially; it already existed in the form of broken branches, and the prehensile hand was perfectly accustomed to grasping such objects. Thus, the first artificial organs were discoveries rather than products of manufacture, and the special intellectual feat associated with them consisted of recognizing that the hand's efficiency could be improved when it was used in conjunction with a foreign object.

The plow was propelled by energy extraneous to the human body. In this case, man succeeded in getting another living creature—the ox harnessed to his plow—to provide an artificial organ with motive power. Thus, the domesticated animal likewise became an artificial organ. Artificial organs may thus be living creatures—above all, fellowmen. The slave was a universally employable artificial organ, and everyone whom we employ to serve us in return for payment likewise becomes our artificial organ for the duration of his service. The word "artificial" thus does not necessarily imply "artificially manufactured" but "artificially appended to our bodily organization."

Every organism from man downward somehow has to acquire or absorb the energy it requires. In plants the source is sunlight; in animals the organic substance which they ingest. Many creatures exploit other sources of power, *e.g.*, wind and water in motion, but the bulk of their energy must always take the roundabout route via their own bodies. To be able to harness energy which, while extraneous to the body, operates directly for its benefit is naturally a tremendous advantage to any organism. Our own progress stems largely from our having perfected this potentiality.

Man's artificial organs have thus become immensely heterogeneous. They are interwoven in the most complex way, and most of them are almost unrecognizable as parts of our physical organization. In one respect, however, they still clearly betray their relationship to our bodies. And here we return to the realm of behavioral research.

Like the majority of our natural organs, each artificial organ requires an appropriate control. Just as all innate functions and modes of behavior depend on hereditarily fixed control formulas, and just as acquired behavior owes its existence to the formation of suitable acquired coordinations, so we require a suitable acquired coordination to service each artificial organ. Even with an artificial organ as simple as an armchair, we must first learn the motor sequence requisite to its use—in other words, how to sit down in it. Large and independently functioning structures such as the railway or a motorcar—both of them artificial organs—likewise require us to "service" them, learn where and how they operate, learn how to harness them to our needs. Important consequences arise from considering things from this angle. In the present book, which deals with peculiarities of human behavior, importance attaches only to the basic principle of this form of power development, which consists in the fact that functional performance has divorced itself from the body, while control—at least partly—rests with the brain.

Rudiments of this, too, exist in animals. Some species use tools. However, the term "artificial organ" is considerably broader than the term "tool"; it embraces every functional unit which serves an organism. In this sense, the spider's web and the bird's nest are also artificial organs.

When an animal uses an existing cave for protection—just as primitive man did—this amounts to the discovery of an artificial organ. Termites' nests and beavers' dams are examples of the communal organ. The degradation of living creatures to the status of artificial organs occurs among the many species of ants which press other species into their service. The acquisition of another individual's services in return for one's own is exemplified by symbiosis and socialization. All these methods of using artificial organs (and of exploiting energy extraneous to the body) are traceable in animals almost exclusively to genetic modifications of the hereditary formula. In terms of achievement, therefore, they cannot be compared with the human development of power.

The animal brain is incapable of acquiring such additional units by means of experience (or the transmission of the same). Admittedly—and here we return to the beginning of this chapter—this required not only a feat of intellect but also an organ appropriate to such a feat. For example, we now know that the dolphin has a highly developed brain, but this avails it little because it could never fashion artificial organs with its fins or harness them to its body. Birds' prehensile feet would be suitable for such purposes, but birds' forelimbs have become modified into wings, so they need their hind legs to stand on. Squirrels might conceivably have developed into creatures with artificial organs, but their bodies are very small, and as we have seen, feats of cerebration require an appropriate number of ganglion cells. Obviously, monkeys could do almost as much with their paws as we with our hands, but in their case the brain is unequal to the task. Discounting minor exceptions, the ape's brain can neither grasp the principles governing the use of artificial organs nor build up the acquired coordinations necessary to their manufacture nor—finally—form the supplementary coordinations essential to the purposive use of artificial organs.

Lorenz, who made an exhaustive study of young apes, found it surprising that they had never developed into anything more than skillful climbers. He was forced to the conclusion that the ancestors of the modern anthropoid possessed a higher degree of intellectual ability. Kortlandt, who spent years observing chimpanzees in the wild, evolved the following hypothesis: The ancestors of the modern chimpanzee actually possessed considerably more intelligence but were hounded from the savanna by the australopithecines—our own ancestors—and forced to return to the primeval forest. Clearly, the savanna was an environment favorable to further development. Thus, according to Kortlandt, the development of the modern anthropoid was reversed by our own ancestors.

Lorenz has drawn attention to another important human characteristic which may be attributable to our ancestors' scansorial way of life. Climbing and, more especially, leaping from branch to branch demand an accurate assessment of spatial dimensions. Prior to leaping, the brain has to form an appropriate idea of the distance involved—a "central spatial representation," as Lorenz terms it.

It is to this circumstance, in his view, that we owe the extremely visual way of thinking which finds expression in our language. We say, for instance, that we "clarify" "obscure" ideas, gain "insights" into things, "see through" someone, "grasp" an idea.

Viewed biologically, therefore, our present stage of progress is in many respects linked with the remote past. Only because the apes developed their prehensile paws by adapting themselves to life in the trees of the primeval forest did the manufacture of artificial organs become practicable in our case. The fact that our ancestors were then forced by climatic changes to adapt themselves to life in the steppe brought about changes in physical organization and, hence, an enlargement of the brain. Finally, the spatial sense acquired in the course of a scansorial phase of existence may have played an equally important role in our further development.

Man may be described as the creature with artificial organs. Our intellect was crucial to this peculiarity, but so were our hands, our power of imagination, and our persistent curiosity. Only the combined effects of all these enabled us to transcend the limitations imposed on our bodily organs. Very slowly at first, then—with the advent of speech and writing—more and more rapidly, we developed and transformed ourselves, acquiring an increasing number of organs which augmented our power and which now, interlaced with almost infinite complexity, span the entire globe.

10

The Barometer of the Soul

D URING our travels through Africa we visited the Olduvai
Gorge where Leakey discovered the earliest-known remains of primitive man (*Zinjanthropus, Homo habilis*)
in 1959 and 1960. According to his preliminary estimate, these
primeval ancestors—who are classified with the australopithecines—lived about 1,000,000 years ago. (More recent computa-
tions have indicated an age of 1,700,000 years.) Leakey found
fragmentary skulls together with various bones, missiles, and
rough-hewn flints. The rock strata in which these fossils were
found lie about 300 feet below the present surface of the surrounding plateau. The Olduvai River had cut a steep and
picturesque gorge through these layers, thereby exposing a
number of these important traces of cultural history. The German zoologist Kattwinkel, who collected butterflies in this area
in 1911 and also visited Olduvai, was the first to discover the
site. From 1931 onward, Leakey carried out extensive excava-
tions in which, in the very deepest layers, level areas surrounded
by stones also came to light. These he interpreted as the remains of shelters.

As other fossils from the same layers showed, the landscape
had not changed substantially since those early days. As a result
of climatic variations the forests had thinned, giving way to
large clearings overgrown with scrub and tall grass in which
lived gazelle, buffalo, and rhinoceros—species which are already
partially extinct today. The principal foes of early man, who

walked erect and lived in groups, were the large feline predators.

It is probable that our human facial movements developed at this time as a form of soundless sign language. Early man could undoubtedly emit sounds akin to those made by the modern ape, but under prevailing circumstances, surrounded by predatory foes and engaged in a quest for easily frightened prey, he must have relied heavily on silent methods of communication. The development of hereditarily fixed facial movements which members of the same species could understand by means of hereditarily fixed mechanisms of innate recognition must therefore have been advantageous to him and must have possessed selective value. This development—one whose existence can only be inferred today—expressed itself physically in a multiplication and differentiation of our facial muscles. This is one of the essential physical differences between us and the modern monkey, which can pull faces but is incapable of performing facial movements as subtle as our own.

Darwin assumed that the movements peculiar to human facial expressions—which still play an important part in communication today—are largely innate and, consequently, that their basic elements are common to all races. One of our main objectives in filming representatives of various races unobserved was to test this hypothesis.

The motion picture is an admirable means of recording and analyzing such phenomena, which makes it all the more surprising that so little use has so far been made of it despite the prevailing interest in human facial expressions. Excellent modern encyclopedias, for instance, present examples of most conceivable forms of animal behavior, from "man running" to "bird flying," but there are few if any 'illustrations entitled "smiling Chinese," "angry Nilotohamite," or "inquisitive American Indian."

In view of this deficiency, we set to work to record a basic inventory of human facial movements. The degree of conformity between individual expressions among different races proved to be so great that it could not be ascribed to learning by imitation. How, then, did the various facial movements come into being, and what was their origin?

As set forth in the first part of this book, many movements

that have, in animals, become ritualized into signals are based on movements of intent which convey an appetency toward specific modes of behavior. In the case of cichlids, we saw that the "Watch out, I'm moving on" signal to their young developed from the movement denoting an intention to swim away. Eibl discovered another example of this form of derivation among tropical mouth cleaners. These extremely agile fish swim into other fishes' mouths and clean them. Fish which desire to be relieved of parasites in this way linger in places where mouth cleaners live, their mouths open wide. The mouth cleaners thereupon start work. As soon as the host fish has had enough, it conveys this by means of a slight but clearly perceptible closing of the mouth, which signifies, "Make your exit, I'm about to shut my mouth." A very simple human facial signal, which probably also originated in a movement of intent, is teeth grinding as a forewarning of the intention to bite. Numerous other mammals—dogs, for instance—perform an analogous movement. The special significance of such a minatory movement is that it does, under certain circumstances, absolve the issuer of the threat from the exertion—and risk—of carrying it out. The signal may alone be sufficient to intimidate an opponent and provoke a withdrawal.

In man, the same signal indicates that our ancestors included some who defended themselves by biting. As we have already mentioned, signals of this type often survive longer than the organs which transmit them. The stag, for example, still grinds its teeth as a threat, even though it now defends itself with antlers and hoofs instead. Much the same applies in our own case. When he bares his canines in anger by drawing back his lips, man is also stressing the significance of organs which have long ceased to be weapons. The obvious conclusion is that our primeval ancestors possessed better-developed canines—as the gorilla still does today.

The teeth-grinding example may also serve to illustrate the origins of the receptive mechanism associated with this signal. This probably took shape before the signal became ritualized. Grinding the teeth is, as we have said, a very primitive and widespread movement of intent which conveys a readiness to bite. Hence, it was of advantage to members of the same species

—and other species as well—to possess a receptive mechanism which, at sight of such a procedure, told them, "Take care, this creature is in a biting mood!" Once such an innate mechanism of recognition, which enjoined due caution, had taken shape, the basis for subsequent ritualization was given. An intensified and exaggerated grinding of the teeth conveyed, with even greater clarity, "Take care, I'm about to bite!"

As soon as one examines the origination of human facial movements from this angle, that which is commonplace and familiar takes on an extremely complicated aspect. In fact, many of our facial signals are a combination of various basic movements. Lorenz showed in the case of dogs that the symptoms of three different intensities of aggressive mood can be compounded with three different intensities of flight intention, and that superimpositions of this kind can produce nine different facial expressions. In human beings the position is even more complicated; on the one hand because we are capable of a much greater number of much more subtly graduated basic movements, and on the other because hereditarily fixed movements are augmented still further by movements which we acquire through imitation and which are thus influenced by the cultural domain in which we grow up.

Our films showed that the different races express interest, for example, in a very similar manner, employing various movements which additionally convey intensity of interest. The face may at first remain immobile, interest being expressed merely by the direction of the eyes. Then mounting interest manifests itself in an opening of the sensory orifices designed to admit as many messages to the brain as possible. There is a widening of the eyes—the most important of such orifices—and the head turns in the appropriate direction. Among primitive men, this simple procedure no doubt possessed importance as a signal to the young and to other members of the clan, who could deduce from it where the center of interest lay—a potentially important piece of information to those out hunting or in danger. If the clan leader, normally the most experienced individual, had noticed something, the ability to indicate its position silently might well be crucial in the next few moments.

A further sign of interest, as Darwin himself noted, is the

opening of the mouth. It is still debatable whether this stems from the relaxing of the jaw muscles—in consequence of heightened attention—or whether it is an aid to keener hearing. Darwin inclined to the second alternative but pointed out that man breathes more quietly through the mouth, which can certainly be an advantage when listening intently. On the other hand, this expression of surprised interest may also contain a hint of fear. The mouth opens wide when fear is intense, and all forms of exertion are accompanied by a deep reflex intake of breath. Thus the open mouth may also betray a readiness to protect oneself from danger or evade it. Simple as it is, this single expression shows how difficult analysis can be.

Another natural sign of interest or curiosity is the inclination of the head, which frequently cocks itself on one side and describes lateral or circular movements. Inclining the head brings not only the eyes and ears but also the nose closer to the object of interest, and there may be an associated intake of breath designed to improve the perception of smells. The oblique posture is probably an aid to acoustic localization, while lateral or circular motions help improve spatial vision and enable one to investigate the object in question from various angles. Another sign of heightened attention, and one which we recorded a number of times, is the involuntary raising of the hand to the mouth or nose. This may again denote an overlay of fear, in that bringing the hand up to the sensory orifices may serve to protect them in case of need. Often, too, a timid person can be seen holding a hand in front of his face as if trying to hide behind it.

If the emotion of fear becomes still more intense, the head remains inclined and the eyes stay wide open, but the investigatory hand movements cease. Like most animals, man tends to freeze into immobility when alarmed or frightened. By so doing, a creature attracts less attention to itself and has a better chance of being overlooked by an enemy. The immobility of the interested observer also has its roots in this innate fear reaction. With increasing distrust, as we call interest which is overlaid with fear, head and body retract and tend to swivel sideways. These are movements of intent denoting a readiness to turn away and flee. The eyes narrow in order to protect the organs of sight. The mouth closes, and intense distrust often expresses itself additionally in a twitching of the nose. The latter movement may be an indication that some of our ancestors were still capable of closing their nostrils at will.

Some of these movements became ritualized into special signals. For instance, our method of conveying disdain—to which Darwin devoted particular attention—consists of several expressive movements: a raising and half-turning of the head, a narrowing of the eyes, and a simultaneous expulsion of air through the nose. The raising of the head may be either a preliminary to flight or a symptom of the wish to impress, which in man, as in animals, consists in making oneself look as big and imposing as possible. The rest is ritualized distrust. By shutting off our sensory orifices, turning away from someone, and exhaling, we are saying, "I don't want anything to do with you. I don't want to see, hear, or smell you. I reject even the air that emanates from you!" Combined with the raising of the head, this is a succinct way of conveying, "I look down on you—you smell bad!"

Movements denoting interest and attention also became ritualized, though in a more subtle way. If one man turns deliberately to face another and regards him with an open gaze, this is an expression of trust. A sudden opening of the eyes is a very primitive token of joyful surprise. A somewhat less emphatic opening of the eyes, accompanied by a raising of the eyebrows, became symptomatic of friendly salutation and liking. This movement, which is probably also innate in us, is particularly common among flirtatious women. A similar arching of the eyebrows in conversation became a sign of heightened attention. In the contrasting case of repudiation—a refusal to look at something we dislike—the eyes tend to close. Similarly, we shut our eyes in a wholly reflex manner when contemplating an idea that alarms us.

Darwin took the view that human movements of intent are explicable in terms of habit—in other words, of acquired associations. Contrary to the now widespread belief that he tried to explain evolution solely by the principle of natural selection, Darwin—like Lamarck—was really of the opinion that acquired characteristics could be inherited. "Some actions, which were at first performed consciously, have become through habit and association converted into reflex actions and are now... firmly fixed and inherited..." he wrote in explanation of his first principle governing the development of expressions in man. Modern behavioral research agrees with Darwin in believing that human expressive movements had a "natural and independent origin"; in other words, that they were not performed "voluntarily and consciously for the attainment of this special end." Instead, they were preexistent and quite involuntary movements from which, by way of ritualization, the various signals peculiar to human facial expression have developed.

In animals, ritualization also led to organic changes and special developments, which helped to increase the effectiveness of signals still further. Eibl suggests that the surviving tufts of hair above our eyes—our eyebrows—may likewise be construed in this sense. If so, this hair owes its survival not only to its useful function of protecting our eyes from the sweat of our brow but also to its function as a means of emphasizing the optical greeting. In Eibl's view, the fact that girls spend so much time on their eyebrows fits in well with this hypothesis. By painting them and tracing their outlines, they not only show off their eyes to better advantage but enhance their signaling powers. A permanent and conspicuous signal (*e.g.,* a surprised expression) can also be created in this way.

One sign of distrust so far unmentioned is the vertical furrowing of the brow. This movement probably originated in the quite analogous wrinkling of the brow which occurs when we stare fixedly at something in bright light—doubtless a frequent and important procedure among our early forebears. In this case the formation of wrinkles served to shade the eyes, and the muscular tension probably aided accurate focusing. Since our mode of thinking is visually orientated, as we have already pointed out, it would not be surprising if this sign of intense contemplation had been transferred to intense inward contemplation as well. Man certainly performs the same movement while meditating, especially when he encounters a mental obstacle. Distrust likewise entails a mental problem, so the formation of wrinkles may be interpreted as an additional expression of the same emotion. Quite similar wrinkles represent another form of minatory signal. Here again they are a symptom of increased mental activity and of the determination to overcome resistance.

Children have practically no facial lines to begin with. These take shape in accordance with the facial movements performed in life, which is why people with certain predominant facial expressions develop lines which betray their basic disposition. One very distinct innate movement is the raising or lowering of the corners of the mouth as an indication of mood. In caricature, a face may be converted into a comic or tragic mask by these lines alone.

To what extent are such innate basic movements influenced by upbringing and tradition? Our films supplied numerous clues to this problem, too.

Many of the races we filmed give vent to facial expressions with the freedom and uninhibitedness of children. This lack of constraint is exemplified by the Samoans, whose self-assured attitude toward life is symbolized by their huts, which are open on all sides. They do not hesitate to expose their private lives to the gaze of others. The play of emotion in their faces is no less undisguised. We filmed some equally direct expressions among the Turkana and Karamojo of Kenya, proud tribes which have scarcely been touched by civilization. The most expressive faces we encountered were those of some Shom Pen whom we met on Great Nicobar Island in the Bay of Bengal and who had had very little contact with white civilization.

Among other races we found facial movements inhibited, evidently by traditional influences. In those instances, man had developed a sort of control mechanism which held direct expressions in check. This was illustrated with particular clarity by films made in Banares, India, where we encountered masklike, immobile faces which conveyed both the Indians' resigned approach to life and the special aura surrounding the holy city. In one such sequence, I recorded how a boy of about eight started to laugh—then froze again as if laughter were forbidden. In the Far East, self-control is deemed essential. Conversations which we filmed in Japan also clearly illustrated this control mechanism for the suppression of outward emotion.

In Europe we met a third stage of development. Here—particularly among the Southern races—facial expressions tend to be exceptionally pronounced but artificial. The original facial movements are employed more or less deliberately—in other words, manipulated. Man has here succeeded in intensifying his innate facial signals, or in using them to simulate feelings which are not present in him. This is a product of custom—in particular, of tact, courtesy, and culture. Sympathy is feigned, where none exists, simply for reasons of politeness. One man smiles at another even when ill-disposed toward him, either as a mark of breeding or in order to avoid dissension. In conversation, the face of the listener often echoes what the other person is saying. If the latter says something serious, the listener grows serious; if he speaks of a surprise, the listener performs a facial movement conveying the same. This, too, is convention rather than genuine fellow feeling. The distinction between the sincere and the histrionic becomes extraordinarily difficult. One can see, even with children, how intellect gains sway over facial movements and employs them for specific purposes. The development of controls subordinate to the will takes place quite unconsciously. These controls are based on the imitation of adult behavior.

Ritualization naturally extends to acquired behavior passed on by tradition—hence the origin of the word. Within the context of good manners, for example, there arise large numbers of movements—some of them tiny but clearly perceptible—which are employed in particular cultural zones and cannot be understood elsewhere. Especially well-differentiated forms occur in the domain of gesture, of which more will be said in a later chapter. In ceremonies, cult rituals, and the dance, many signals have become so remote from the expressive movements which underly them that their origin can no longer be discerned.

Finally, a still more advanced form of manipulation is exemplified by the actor. In order to convey the prevailing emotions of his part to the audience, he has to put over individual expressions as clearly and convincingly as possible. We got performers to mime such facial expressions for us and thus had an opportunity to compare deliberately simulated expressions with analogous expressions which we covertly photographed in real life. What emerged was that the actor omits inessentials and stresses essentials. With a good actor it is possible to see what characteristics of expression are peculiar to the emission of specific signal effects. Furthermore, in order to achieve special effects, the actor deliberately carries out various superimpositions. Finally, as we found it particularly easy to observe while filming members of the classical Japanese theater, the passage of time stimulates the growth of certain traditional expressions, which represent a sort of secret code linking the actor with his audience.

The visitor from another planet would probably see the anterior surface of our head—our "barometer of the soul"—in quite a different way. It is very probable that we have an innate recognition, not only of the most fundamental and important facial movements, but also of the basic layout of the face itself, which we see as a totality rather than as a sum of mouth, eyes, nostrils, and so on. Thus it is clearly possible for us to dissociate ourselves from this mode of observation and look at a face really objectively. We can, however, create such an illusion momentarily by watching filmed close-ups projected not only at a different speed but upside down as well. What then confronts us is an expanse whose salients and orifices vary their relative positions. This impression—startling in its unfamiliarity—does not last. The brain soon recognizes the subterfuge and reverses the image so that individual features reassume their accustomed pattern.

11

The Friendship Signal

WHY do human beings smile so much? We see smiling faces everywhere—in offices, in shops, on the street. Are we particularly amiable creatures? Behavioral research has shown that we are anything but. Gregarious though he is, man is far from being a model of friendliness. This is precisely why the human smile possesses a special function of very vital significance.

As we have already mentioned, man displays a marked aggressive streak, especially toward his fellowmen. This aggressiveness is a true, innate instinct with a spontaneous ability to arouse excitation and an appetitive behavior of its own. Lorenz has studied this strange and apparently antisocial impulse in animals, and in his book *On Aggression,* from which I have already quoted, he suggests that it affords distinct benefits to them. The aggressive drive ensures, first, that by doing battle with each other animals distribute themselves fairly evenly across the territory available to them—a considerable aid to the specific survival of the species. Second, premating fights between males favor procreation by the strongest—another asset to the species. Third, intraspecific aggression promotes the selective breeding of sturdy defenders of the brood—an advantage to species which practice brood tending. Fourth, the aggressive drive can provide the motive power for other activities. And fifth, in the case of social animals—in which it is particularly strongly developed—

it leads to the formation of a ranking order which helps the ablest individuals to assert their leadership.

On the other hand, the aggressive drive also raises a grave problem. Since mating entails intimate association, the instinctive tendency to remain aloof from members of the same species constitutes a disruptive factor. Brood tending likewise presupposes close contact, and the forming of a community becomes meaningful only when individual members are prepared to cooperate. The aggressive drive could not, therefore, have developed its undeniable advantages without the concomitant growth of other norms of action and reaction which inhibit and counteract this impulse at the biologically correct moment.

Some examples of mechanisms which neutralize the aggressive drive were quoted in the first part of this book. Mentioned, for instance, was the way the male dancing fly offers the female a present, thereby distracting her attention so that copulation can take place. In many of the higher vertebrates—including man—a partner's aversion to physical contact, which is rooted in the aggressive drive, may be diminished by suitably childish behavior so that advances can take place. In the case of brood tending, we find it a matter of course that parents should not only permit their young to approach them but should look after them as well. Actually this is anything but a matter of course. Brood tending requires considerable exertion of parents and substantially curtails their other instinctive behavior. Thus, these "friendly" reactions must also be elicited by appropriate mechanisms. In fact, key stimuli emanating from the young animal are responsible for promoting this behavior. In the case of turkey chicks, for instance, it is their cheeping cries. Inability to hear these will cause the turkey hen to kill her own young. Other key stimuli consist of physical characteristics peculiar to young animals or of other combinations of stimuli perceivable by parents. We have already mentioned that young human beings, too, can elicit such reactions from adults by emitting suitable signal stimuli occasioned by their size, their conformation, and their awkward movements. In addition, there are the child's crying, which arouses our protective instinct, and its smile. The strength of the latter signal should not be underestimated. It creates a personal, binding relationship between child and parents and certainly contributes substantially to bond formation.

The special signals young animals beam at their brood-tending parents—including those of the young human being—therefore help to inhibit aggression and elicit sympathy and goodwill. In the case of crying and smiling (which we shall provisionally regard as associated with laughing), other definite signal meanings come into play. Crying, for instance, means, "I don't feel well." Smiling or laughing, on the other hand, means, "I feel fine." Parents respond to this signal by smiling themselves, which means, in turn, "I love you—you can rely on me." This relieves fear-born tensions and instills confidence. In a Japanese amusement park we filmed the facial expressions of parents watching their toddlers riding in a miniature train. Each time a child passed a parent, its face beamed an unmistakable signal: "Don't worry, I'm here." And: "Well done, we're proud of you." These signals are extremely important to children during their early years and correspond to the routine contact calls used by many other creatures, especially birds. The regular cluck-cluck-cluck of the hen tells the chicks that all is well and confirms her approval of the actions they perform. In human beings the parental smile similarly bolsters the child as it embarks on its first sorties into the uncharted territory of life.

As time passes, the child learns from experience all the things that it can accomplish with its smile and begins to employ it deliberately. This habit persists throughout life, like the dual significance of the smile itself. On the one hand, it courts sympathy and demands "Love me." On the other, it possesses a hortatory significance and says, "I love you—come to me. Rely on me—you can trust me." Both meanings acquire still further force during courtship. One partner smiles at the other seeking to make himself (or herself) as attractive as possible—in other words, to stimulate the other's senses. Again, the smile also signifies: "You may approach me—don't be afraid, you attract me." In everyday community life the smile has become a universal greeting which, like other forms of salutation, has degenerated into a routine cliché. We are brought up to be polite, and everyone learns from personal experience that more can be gotten out of people with smiles and friendly greetings. The occasional intolerance and irascibility of others may be somewhat neutralized by this means. Anyone who omits to smile and greet people for only a few days, whether at work or in private life, will find himself encountering considerable resentment. The fact that even a routine smile still retains its effect is demonstrated with particular clarity by the elicitive function of this signal. The politician who addresses a group of voters or allows himself to be photographed always smiles because he knows that he will ingratiate himself more effectively. The shrewd Chinese have made "Smile at all costs" a universal axiom, and in the United States an entire nation has developed the habit of donning ritualized, magazine-cover-type smiles on every conceivable occasion. A more accurate explanation of why human beings smile so often might well be that we smile because we are not, basically, unfriendly creatures. Thus our smile is a means of eliciting contact readiness in others and of conveying our own accessibility to contact. If we use it as a social bridge builder, we do so not merely because of upbringing or mood, but from sheer necessity.

The large significance of this small signal becomes doubly plain to us whenever we approached native villages in remote parts of Africa. Whenever we were confronted by immobile, inscrutable faces, we knew things could go one way or the other. The suspicious or surly face is an unmistakable warning which arouses uneasiness in the person approaching—not only because of past experience but because of an innate recognitive reaction situated far deeper within us. Let the corners of the mouth curve upward and the first smile dawn, however, and the situation is instantly transformed. Without a single word or gesture, the wearer of the smile conveys that he may be approached and is prepared to greet one in friendly fashion. In our case, whenever we entered a strange village, established contact, and tried to communicate verbally, smiles flew back and forth as a sort of permanent guarantee that we were mutually well disposed—precisely the same guarantee which the growing child requires from its parents.

How did this very important facial signal originate evolutionarily, and what primordial movement underlies it?

Similar friendship-eliciting signals abound in the animal world. Often they originated in movements which already denoted a friendly basic attitude. Among mammals, for instance, it is common for the mother to clean and comb the fur of her young. Because such skin tending is always an expression of a friendly basic attitude, adult animals also clean each other to create a mutually friendly mood. Movements of this kind develop into a form of greeting, as when the dog welcomes us by licking our hand. Among various monkeys (macaques, makis) similiar greeting movements have become even more ritualized. When in a friendly mood, these creatures lick each other and comb each other's fur with their teeth; when greeting each other they perform analogous movements in the air (and chatter at the same time). In other words, they "lick" and "comb" in the direction of those being greeted.

It is also logical that an animal should conceal its own aggression-eliciting characteristics or "weapons" from a potential adversary, if only to allay aggression in others. For example, the laughing gull's conspicuous black head marking provokes aggression in members of its own species. This is why, in the mating ceremony, it averts its head from its partner in a strange form of friendship signal. Storks also swivel their heads in greeting, averting their beaks from the object of their salutation and at the same time rattling them.

Perhaps the strangest source of development of greeting movements is the redirection of hostile behavior. Horses greet each other by opening their muzzles and baring their teeth— a procedure almost identical with the one which they perform as a warning. The sole difference is that the horse pricks its ears in greeting and lays them back flat when in a minatory mood. Lorenz succeeded in ascertaining how such redirections came about and what deeper significance they possess.

The pattern is as follows: Individual A creates a friendship bond with Individual B by threatening Individual C. The forming of a common front against a third party promotes an alliance or pact of friendship of the sort concluded by human beings under similar circumstances. Lorenz was able to trace in cichlids and greylag geese how the bond-forming process has led to a ritualized form of aggression inhibition. A minatory movement initially directed at a mate becomes, by redirection, a threat directed past the mate at a third party (or any other suitable target), and this leads to the forming of the bond. The movement then becomes—to quote Lorenz—"a ritually autonomous appeasement ceremony"; it becomes "an end in itself"—indeed, "a necessity." It is important that each of the two partners can perform the ceremony only with the other individual in question. In practical terms, then, this greeting consists in the first individual's directing a threat movement past the person of the second.

Lorenz holds that the human smile came into being in an analogous way, as a redirected baring of the teeth at a third party. In his view, laughing and smiling are simply varying grades of intensity of the same behavior pattern—"that is, they respond with different thresholds to the same particular quality of excitation." As a special argument he cites the fact that many Japanese look past each other when exchanging broad smiles. Thus, Lorenz construes the smile of greeting as an appeasement ceremony "which, like the triumph ceremony of geese, has evolved through ritualization of a redirected threat."

Eibl defined his approach to this subject in *Handbuch der Biologie*. To him, smiles and laughter have "a common root but seem to have become ritualized in different ways." The smile often turns into laughter, which may thus be interpreted as smiling of a higher intensity—"but not only as such." Other actors are involved—for example, laughter is characterized by an open mouth and the rhythmical emission of sounds.

Darwin, who dealt with the same facial expression, took the view that laughter was originally a manifestation of sheer joy or pure happiness. He noted the frequency with which imbeciles and mental deficients smile, and this strengthened him in his belief. In most cases, it was impossible for their happy excitation to be associated with a specific idea: They simply felt pleasure and expressed it by laughing and smiling. Thus, Darwin reasoned, laughter was either a more fully developed smile or—more probably—a smile was the last vestige of a habit of laughter which had become firmly rooted in the course of many generations. Darwin found it "an obscure point," or not important, that the corners of the mouth should retract, raising the upper lip. His conjecture was that the movement originated in the need to open the mouth as widely as possible in order to emit a "full and abundant" sound.

In one of our television films I tried to present the smile as a redirected threat, as Lorenz interpreted it to be. However, the more I analyzed our film, the more unlikely this interpretation seemed. None of the sequences of people smiling (or laughing) at others conveyed the least suggestion of "indirect tooth baring"—in other words, of redirection. Instead, they seemed to support Darwin's theory that smiles and laughter were originally both related manifestations of a happy mood. Although Darwin never noted the smile's function as an aggression buffer, this interpretation can also be made to conform with his view. The smile—directed at another person—would then mean, "I'm happy to see you." And it could also mean, "Don't be afraid to approach me." Since smiling and laughing exert a mood-transmissive effect, they were able to induce a better humor and greater accessibility to contact in other people as well.

The more I compared laughter and smiling, however, the more clearly the two phenomena diverged. Smiling invariably contains an element of entreaty, friendliness, and appeasement, but always a latent "I am good to you." Laughter, however, invariably has something aggressive about it—often something mocking and contemptuous. Thus let us consider a few arguments to support the contention that these two signals are totally different, both in significance and origin.

First, laughter. What excites this reaction in the most rudimentary instances? Something laughable, of course. But what strikes us as laughable? We are often impelled to laugh by the spectacle of others' misfortunes and the agreeable realization that we have been spared the thing that has befallen them. Laughter and mockery are closely related, and this brings us back to the situation in which two or more individuals deride others of their kind—a circumstance which Lorenz quite rightly regards as a symptom of aggression and, at the same time, an aid to bond formation. Joint derision is related to the expulsion reaction commonly observed in animals, which is usually elicited by malformation or, in more general terms, by the quality of being different, physically or behaviorally, from the group.

The result of this reaction is that the outsider is not only expelled but in certain circumstances killed. The directing of concerted threats at an enemy is called hating. In primates, this behavior is accompanied by a rhythmical emission of sounds strongly reminiscent of human laughter. On the one hand, therefore, such procedures lead to the forming of united fronts, and on the other, they afford an opportunity of working off pent-up aggression on a specific object which can thus become a surrogate.

I was nevertheless impressed, while watching our films of people laughing, by the extent to which this signal beautifies any face and enlists fellow feeling. I filmed a Chinese market woman during an outburst of fury and again, ten minutes later, while smiling. In the first instance her face was repellent; in the second—although she was no beauty—positively attractive.

If we regard laughing and smiling as two distinct phenomena, it is clear that each occurs in every conceivable grade of intensity. In light laughter the rhythmical emission of sound is reduced to silent expulsions of breath occurring in rapid succession or may consist of only one such exhalation or a suggestion of the same. With a smirk there is no expulsion of breath at all, and the lips are only slightly retracted—yet even this is not the same as smiling. Smiling, in turn, may attain an intensity verging on rapture without turning into laughter—in other words, without the emission of sounds.

The two signals are alike in possessing a strongly infectious quality. With the smile, this is inherent to its placatory function. Laughter is known to be particularly infectious, but its effect is usually limited to a group. An outsider may often be induced to join in a smile, but laughter within a closed group is more likely to excite an outsider's annoyance, especially if he is ignorant of its cause, because he assumes it to be directed at himself.

This is where the basic functional difference between laughter and smiling becomes particularly apparent. If we encounter a stranger and laugh at him on sight, he will probably interpret it as a sign of derision and disparagement rather than as a greeting. If we smile at him, all misunderstanding is precluded. There is nothing aggressive about the smile. It says clearly, "I am pleased to see you" and beyond that, "I am prepared to welcome and possibly assist you."

The behavior of persons taking leave of one another is very informative in this respect. Here the smile becomes a sort of summary of the encounter and says, "I am still well disposed toward you and shall continue to greet you in a friendly fashion." If leave takers have laughed heartily while together, the summary may well contain an echo of that laughter. The persons concerned may even slap each other laughingly on the back, as if to say, "We had some good laughs together." If no laughter has occurred during an encounter, a parting laugh has the very obvious effect of insulting and disparaging the other party.

When people who have laughed heartily together during a previous encounter meet again, laughter may become a form of greeting. Laughter here becomes a reminder of an earlier meeting—of a bond which was cemented by joint laughter. Unconstrained laughter is a widespread greeting, especially among young people. In full accord with the Lorenzian interpretation, it then represents an allusion to a pact which has already been concluded.

Furthermore, though obviously as a secondary function, laughter has become an outlet for excitation. The English philosopher Herbert Spencer pointed out as early as 1863 that energy which is obstructed in its flow can take another direction and erupt in the form of laughter. In modern terminology, this would be called displacement laughter, though it is not certain whether the energy born of different motivation actually "jumps the tracks" or merely initiates the movement. Whatever the truth, this is the origin of embarrassed, nervous, hysterical, or even angry laughter. No further illustration is needed of how difficult it is to distinguish between the two signals and why we are prone to regard them as different rungs of the same ladder. Of course a smile can also be embarrassed, shamefaced, or nervous. In this case, the friendship signal is superimposed upon the expression of fear or shame appropriate to the circumstances or, alternatively, is associated with signs of excitation.

Laughter's supplementary function as a means of discharging

excitation may also explain why the mentally disturbed so often indulge in it. Their much-frustrated instincts find laughter to be an outlet, so their laughter is not the primitive sign of happiness assumed by Darwin. Normal laughter expressive of good humor can also be construed as a product of happy excitation in general, so it would then be an expression of a secondary rather than of the original function. The frequent transition from smiling to laughter may be explained in the same way. This can be described as displacement laughter which gives expression to the happy excitation of reunion.

Finally, as for Japanese looking past one another when smiling broadly, a more logical explanation of such behavior lies in the fact that courtesy is normally exaggerated among the Japanese, a fact which manifests itself in highly refined movements of the face and head. As we have already mentioned, a fixed stare inspires fear and provokes resistance; it is a form of behavior which precedes attack. If the stare is combined with a smile its effect is normally neutralized and our uneasiness abates. The Japanese evidently prefer to rule out even this suggestion of potential uneasiness, so they either look past other people when conversing with them or gaze at the ground. This is certainly not a relic of erstwhile aggression, especially in a race whose manners are so strongly influenced by tradition. Rather, it is one of the numerous conventions which make it so difficult for the European to understand the Oriental.

If laughter and smiling are, in fact, different signals, how did smiling really orginate? From what primordial movements was it ritualized?

Darwin pointed out in his principle of antithesis that expressive movements may also be explained by the fact that they are of a directly opposite nature to another expressive movement. For example, if the head is shaken from side to side on the basis of a primordial movement to convey no, there can be no clearer affirmative signal than the contrary movement—in other words, a nod.

Darwin specifically demonstrated this principle by the example of the expressive movements of the dog and cat. When a German shepherd approaches with hostile intent, it walks stiffly with head raised. The tail is also held erect and quite rigid, the hairs on back and neck bristle, the ears are directed forward, and the gaze is fixed. When the same dog approaches its master, the head is lowered, the body tends to grovel and squirm, the tail is lowered and wagged, the ears are drawn back, and the eyes lose their fixed stare. The cat, on the other hand, crouches and prepares to pounce when in a hostile mood. The tail is fully extended and thrashes laterally to and fro, the ears are flattened, and the jaws part to emit a hiss or growl. When caressing its master, the animal adopts an exaggeratedly upright stance, its back slightly arched, its tail rigid and vertical, its ears erect and pricked. It keeps its mouth closed and purrs. In each case the aggressive stance is undoubtedly the original one, and each individual symptom of mood possesses a biological import of its own. The symptoms of the opposite mood—of friendliness and accessibility to contact—are simply the contrary of the first set. They have no special meaning for the most part, merely the function of looking as dissimilar from their counterparts as possible.

This principle makes it possible to construe smiling as the antithesis of the human facial expression which conveys ill humor. This has four main features: compressed lips, a mouth drawn downward at the corners, vertical furrows in the forehead, and a slight jutting of the lips. Compressed lips are a symptom of tension, determination, and obstinacy. The down-turned corners of the mouth are probably attributable to a muscular movement suppressive of cries or weeping. The vertical furrows in the forehead also express tension, and the jutting lips are a very ancient signal of which the chimpanzee provides a clear demonstration when angry. On such occasions it extends its lips like a tube, a movement observable in human beings among stubborn children, especially those of primitive tribes. All these characteristics are expressive of rage, ill temper, annoyance, and sullen obstinacy—in other words, of a mood diametrically opposed to the approachable. If one wished to devise a signal which clearly expressed a friendly and accommodating attitude, it would take the following form: a smooth brow, a relaxed and open mouth, and retracted lips drawn upward at the corners—all of them characteristics of the human smile.

In our primitive forebears' communities it must have been

extremely important to a child to know when it was permissible or inadvisable to approach an adult. The same applied equally to adults encountering strangers. The angry, ill-tempered, or sick individual could be dangerous if approached too closely by those who encroached on his private territory. In this context, it was extremely important for man to develop an innate recognition mechanism which would give him suitable warning on sighting such a face. It was just as important for man to develop an appropriate signal for the contrary mood—a sign of approachability. And this, as we have seen, became further strengthened into a means of inhibiting aggression and actively enlisting fellow feeling.

Within the framework of the social orders created by man—a subject which we shall be discussing in the next chapter—the human being succeeded in erecting invisible barriers between himself and other members of his species. Particularly where a community waxed in numbers and a strict ranking order grew up, there arose barriers of convention which often became so rigid in the course of history that it was virtually impossible to penetrate them. Although the caste and class systems have relaxed in our modern society, rigid divisions still exist. We can ask another man for the time or some other piece of information, we can beg a light or some other small favor, but these are no more than temporary gaps in a wall which does not really crumble until we are linked—or introduced—by a suitable third party.

The smile has always been an arrow which pierced these invisible barriers. We owe our present position of supremacy to cooperation, and the smile has fulfilled the important function of bringing us aggressive creatures closer together. By smiling—whether the smile be genuine or assumed—we ingratiate ourselves with other people and bind them to us. The intricate network of human civilization can be said to owe its cohesion to a myriad-and-one such smiles.

12

Man and Order

ANYONE who observes fish in a coral reef will note a definite regularity to their movements. Instead of moving to and fro at random, they observe property rights and exhibit quite rigidly determined behavioral patterns. Many species live in particular areas and defend them vigorously against encroaching rivals; others have specialized in methods of food acquisition of which they alone are capable. Only a limited number of fish can practice one such method in any one reef. If similar or different species encounter one another, their reactions are so uniform that one can often predict the course of events in advance. Again, if one compares the pattern of existence prevailing in one reef with that which prevails in another, similarities also become apparent. Here as there, a similar balance of power arises from innate behavioral patterns and a similar environmental situation.

Our hypothetical visitor from another planet would note similar phenomena if he looked down on a metropolitan city. He would see that individual human beings follow dissimilar forms of existence by reason of special behavioral patterns and with the aid of artificial organs. As in the coral reef, individual groups dominate specific areas which they vigorously defend. Here again, each area can only sustain so many individuals who follow the same occupation. Here, as there, a balance of power prevails which is typical of the area in question and which may take a form very similar to that which prevails in areas of similar structure.

One major difference is that a very complex division of labor prevails in the world of man, and that certain forms of behavior are prohibited. For instance, the individual is constrained from physically harming his fellowmen, appropriating their artificial organs, or forcibly converting them into artificial organs. What behavior is permitted and what is not are set down somewhere in the form of community formulas, and additional institutions such as the police and judiciary are given the responsibility to implement them. Thus, what is involved here is not just a form of order that can be explained as a natural state of equilibrium in society. In the world of man, some activities are promoted by a division of labor and others are barred—a process which results in a deliberately created social order.

How did these orders—which are peculiar to man—come into being? Where are their formulas, and how are they controlled? Has something entirely new to the animal kingdom supervened in evolution, or are there evolutionary links between the accomplishments of animals and the products of human organizing ability?

In Naberera, a remote district of Tanganyika, we visited a prehistoric watering place to which the neighboring Masai still drive their cattle as they have for centuries. The water lies at the bottom of several deep cavities reached by ravinelike paths. At the end of these paths, troughlike indentations have been hollowed out of the rock. The Masai scoop up the water with their leather bags which they empty into the troughs. We set up our camera in a commanding positon and left it running.

The resulting film shows how a Masai drives his herd down the gorge, climbs into the hole, and starts to draw water. He is naked, and his leather bag—a very primitive form of artificial organ—seems to be a living extension of his hands. Speeded up, the film demonstrates the extraordinary regularity of his scooping motions. This is an acquired coordination which has been handed down by imitation and is perfectly performed. Its deliberate rationalization distinguishes it from similar acquired coordinations present in animals. Man could never succeed in performing a motor pattern with such economy of effort if he were incapable of self-observation.

A second Masai comes down the path, lays his spear aside, and joins his companion in the hole. The two men proceed to draw water together. One stoops and fills the pouch; the other takes it and empties it into the trough. The pouch travels up and down without the slightest interruption, the movements of both men being so perfectly coordinated that they might be muscles on the same arm. Three basic principles of increased human efficiency are manifest here: First, a purposive procedure is broken down into parts which can be performed by different individuals; second, the individual specializes in his share of the work and does his best to rationalize it as far as possible; and third, the various part-actions are so regulated as to produce a performance flow which transcends the individual.

Animals have innate forms of recognition which, in turn, activate innate motor coordinations. Similarly, the ability to recognize particular stimulus situations can also be *acquired* in animals, and key stimuli of this type can bring about the activation of *acquired* motor sequences. The extremely simple form of collaboration practiced by the two water drawers might be explained in terms of the same principle. To the first man, the handing down of the empty pouch is the stimulus situation which prompts him to take, fill, and hoist it; and that, in turn, is a signal to the second man to take the pouch, empty it into the trough, and hand it back. These two basic working procedures have always been inherent throughout the entire range of human collaboration, however complicated it may be in detail. Man has to acquire two abilities in order to engage in such collaboration. First, he must learn how to carry out particular motor sequences, which entails the formation of appropriate control formulas in his brain. And second, he must learn to recognize when, where, and in relation to what extraneous stimuli the procedures in question should be put into effect. These basic accomplishments are thus a further development of behavior which is also practicable to animals. Man's peculiarity consists solely in grasping the expediency of collaboration—an intellectual feat of which we shall have more to say later.

The water drawers illustrate yet another important principle.

The artificial organ they employ—a leather pouch—does not actually belong to either of them from the functional point of view. Like the two men themselves, it has become part of a productive process. As human collaboration gains in complexity, so this phenomenon emerges more clearly. The human participants and their various artificial organs become components of a totality which transcends the individual, parts of an invisible body which we term organization. Like tools, machines, and other means of production used in such a work-sharing system, man does no more than fulfill a function and perform a task. The larger modern factories demonstrate how true this is. If one unit ceases to operate, a substitute has to be devised—and many functions can be fulfilled by either a man or a machine. It is the performance of a functional component which matters, not its structure. For as long as human beings collaborate within the framework of such an organized body, they cease to be individuals proper and become organs themselves.

The motor formula necessary to any such collaboration is the actual order of the productive system. Initially, this may still be rooted in the brains of the participants, as in the case of the water drawers. Once collaboration gains in scope and complexity, however, this function detaches itself from those who perform it and becomes a unit in its own right, a special organ which henceforward assumes control. In a large factory the individual production formulas are the fruit of mental exertion by hundreds of people; laid down in plans, drawings, and directives, they forsake the human brain and themselves become artificially created functional units. The control function likewise is divorced and is taken over by specialized units—directors, foremen, and so on. Today even this task devolves partly or wholly upon artificially created functional units, namely, computers.

The relationship between bodies of human collaboration and animal and vegetable bodies becomes plain when viewed from this angle. Each of these bodies is characterized by a particular order which is, and must be, tailored to a very particular task. This order originates quite differently in organisms than in human organizations, yet the required appearance of the order in question is little affected thereby. All that really matters in each case is that the order be expedient, in other words, that it should facilitate the task to be performed. If an animal or vegetable body or a body of human collaboration performs the task for which it is equipped, it is "in order." If it fails to do so, it is not. The same applies to each separate unit which helps to constitute that body—to each of its organs, in fact.

Of course a distinction must be drawn between temporal and spatial order. So far we have referred exclusively to the coordination of motor procedures, that is, to orders governed by the passage of time. But these, again, are made possible only by a spatial order, by the juxtaposition and interposition of individual functional units. A spatial order of this type is equally important—indeed, essential—to every organism, whether animal or vegetable, and to every human organization. Only if heart, bones, blood vessels, etc., bear a very particular relationship to all the other units in the system will the body be capable of an orderly motor procedure occurring in the dimension "time" (*i.e.*, of the behavior appropriate to it). Precisely the same conditions exist in every factory. Only an appropriate spatial arrangement of bays, personnel, machines, and so on renders the productive process possible.

There is, however, one form of spatial order which made its appearance only with man: the "keeping in order" of material objects. This form of order has to do with our artificial organs and is a concomitant of the fact that they are not an integral part of our bodies. We lay them aside and must take note of their exact location so as to have them available when required. The more numerous they are, the greater the problem. Keeping in order (together with the provision of necessary safeguards) thus represents another mortgage with which these useful structures are encumbered. Where our natural organs are concerned, only memory storage presents a comparable problem. We have yet to discover how the brain manages to make memories available when needed. We stow away our artificial organs (if small) in boxes, pigeonholes, and drawers. We label many with letters and numbers; we record others in inventories.

The forms of order so far discussed (apart from the keeping in order of material objects) are peculiar to man only to the extent that he created them deliberately, whereas they took shape—quite passively—in animals and plants by way of a gradual selective process. The order most truly characteristic of man—yet another variety—arises from the fact that individual purposive procedures have a tendency to impinge. Until now we have referred solely to methods of increasing efficiency which man has evolved by creating superindividual organizations. The resulting productive systems do, however, tend to conflict—that is to say, one order obstructs another. This becomes clear when two people wish to cross a footbridge too narrow to accommodate both of them. One of the two must wait, interrupting the flow of purposive movement. Which one has to give way?

In the coral reef a natural equilibrium grows up among the creatures living there, based on the relative strength of the individual species. In human society, man uses specialization and collaboration to form productive bodies which are no less diverse in structure and behavior than animals and plants. They too compete, and here too there is an adjustment of relative strength quite similar to the natural (ecological) equilibrium governing animals and plants in nature. It is man's peculiarity to have created orders which intervene in this trial of strength and control it.

Man thus created an order of orders: the state. In this particularly broad form of organization, human beings and all the productive bodies created by them are subject to certain rules and restrictions, or laws. The extent to which individual freedom of action is curtailed differs widely according to the nature of a particular order.

These exceptionally highly integrated orders, which the life process succeeded in imposing on man, became disseminated throughout the globe. Their structure, too, is necessarily similar to that of organisms. They, too, consist of organs which must fulfill appropriate functions within the total work-sharing system. Their behavioral formulas, too, have become separate units known as constitutions. These huge living bodies, too, are in competition and conflict with one another. The creation of a universal order which embraced all of them would be an even higher—on this planet, the supreme—stage of integration.

However, still other forms of orders have played their part in human evolution. They have contributed less to increased efficiency than to the fulfillment of other human aspirations which stem partly from innate and instinctive behavior.

First, there are the ranking orders of human society. As we have already mentioned, animals which live in communities evolve similar arrangements, which lay down power relationships and determine, for instance, which individual takes precedence at feeding places or in the satisfaction of sexual urges. Such orders have been closely studied in the cases of chickens and monkeys. Where man is concerned, the nature of his organizations has inevitably led to the growth of hierarchically constructed chains of command; moreover, the individual's degree of seniority is of great importance in social life. What substantially contributes to this is our strongly developed impulse to dominate others or be dominated by them. Each impulse brings its own satisfaction. To obey a person whom we respect can be as satisfying as to lead others. Apart from that, the human urge to dominate—in conjunction with the sexual and brood-tending urges—prompts us to aspire to positions of eminence and esteem. Although these tendencies are not dissimilar to those observable in animals, it is an additional human peculiarity that in our case differences of rank are often associated with legal prerogatives, and that such prerogatives have become hereditary by way of tradition and law. Thanks to the prerogatives of privileged classes, therefore, the universally necessary principle of order was rendered more complicated and difficult by legislation.

Other interesting orders are those which we call custom and usage. They represent communal practices which have been crystallized by upbringing and education. These rules for living differ widely in different parts of the world and are mainly concerned with birth, mating, brood tending, and death. Beyond that, they concern the way in which we eat, live, and treat other people, our modes of greeting and speech, how we behave in a given situation, and what we should abstain from. Some of the appropriate guidance formulas are written down, but most are transmitted from one brain to the next verbally and by demonstration. When such rules are infringed, the community itself functions as judge, and social sanctions serve as punishment. As with every pattern of behavior which has become habitual, these communal habits are associated with corresponding appetencies. The community clings to them stubbornly and becomes restive if prevented from indulging them by some outside agency. As the world became increasingly organized, these patterns overlapped more and more; many of them reduced others to absurdity, and new ones of wider scope took shape. The modern preference is for dismantling anything conducive to restriction, while retaining anything connected with sensual pleasure and, if possible, reinforcing it still further.

The most durable—and at the same time, mysterious—forms of order man has evolved are his religions. The very fact that such large numbers of these sprang up indicates that man had a need for them. Being rooted in supersensual ideas—of which more will be said later—they are not susceptible of practical examination. This, presumably, is one reason why man clings to them with such peculiar obstinacy.

Does man have an innate impulse toward order?

Keeping in order did not become established with man until he started to use artificial organs in considerable numbers, or barely 10,000 years ago. A form of instinctive behavior cannot be expected to have adapted itself to our changed requirements in what is, from the biological aspect, a short period of time. On the other hand an impulse toward coordinated movement—in other words, toward the development of formulas for purposive motor procedures—can be observed in any child. This, after all, is what children aspire to when they play with constructional toys, and this is what rewards them with feelings of joy and triumph at the creation of each successful motor pattern. The same clearly perceptible impulse persists in the adult. All constructive work and everything creative in humankind is an endeavor to carry out purposive movements and create purposive spatial structures. This is the source of those feelings of happiness and contentment which are associated with every successful piece of work. Coordinated movement also holds an appeal for us, as witness the impression the sight of a ballet company or a body of men marching with perfect precision makes on us. We are similarly attracted by spatial coordination, which is why we are delighted by the symmetry and harmony of architecture. All this suggests that the recognition of and striving for coordinated spatiotemporal complexes is hereditarily anchored in man, either as a genuine instinct (closely associated, perhaps, with that of curiosity) or as an innate learning disposition.

Order—the essential formula for every form of achievement—links our highest human achievements with every successful development of the life process—yes, even with its earliest beginnings. The first living molecules were in themselves a spatial order which brought about a very specific process, *i.e.*, a temporal order. In the course of time, as the most primitive surviving organisms clearly show, a division of labor arose between individual components: Functional units were developed. There also came into being guidance formulas which enabled organisms to multiply, or construct additional identical orders. The cohesion of such life units, or cells, led to the formation of more highly integrated collaborative units. Although the formula for the development of these multicellular bodies continued to be the same units as before, *i.e.*, the hereditary formula, a new specialized unit—the central nervous system—was developed for the control of movement. There were now two alternatives: Either the behavior of a living creature was controlled by *innate* norms of action and reaction, or the individual had first to build up such norms in the course of its personal battle with environment. Creatures controlled by instinct were better equipped to become specialists, but learners were more adaptable. As a learner, man succeeded because of various favorable prerequisites in overcoming the limitations of his natural organs: He extended his power through artificial functional units. Although divorced from his body, these required control—and the appropriate formulas at first remained in his brain. When several people worked together, these formulas became distributed among the brains involved, and artificial organs lost their clear connection with the individual. In the course of further development, the control formula in such organizations detached itself from the individual brain in the guise of written or diagrammatic instructions whose implementation became the concern of still more specialized units.

As a result, superindividual productive bodies developed which displayed fundamental differences from animals and plants: Their parts were not conjoined, they consisted largely of quite different materials, and they came into being quite differently. Nevertheless, they embodied a continuation of the same principle. Their order followed from the task to be performed.

No reference has been made in this chapter to the motive power which has led to this vast development—the will to power in the Nietzschean sense. But whatever its true nature, only orders made the growth of efficiency possible.

13

Gestures

IN the course of a single day a man's hands perform many, many superfluous and pointless movements. They lead a life of their own, almost as if they were living creatures in their own right, when their owner is talking. They reach into the air, grasp it, knead it, spar with it, perforate it with outstretched fingers. What is the significance of these motions? Considering all the purposeful actions our hands perform, these disorderly movements strike a jarring note.

Scrutinizing them more closely, we encounter an important evolutionary principle. Lack of order can, without deliberate intent, give birth to order. Even quite fortuitous concomitants can acquire significance for a living creature, become functional and, thus, useful. Natural selection then ensures that the new feature gains ground. What was originally fortuitous becomes a new order.

Human gestures are a good example of this development. Many of them can be traced back to quite meaningless movements of the sort which can still be observed in any agitated person. Like facial movements, these gestures developed into signals which were clarified and simplified by ritualization. The bulk of them were passed on by tradition, *i.e.,* learned, but there are probably many others which have already attained hereditary fixation or exist in the form of learning dispositions. The recognition of these signals, on the other hand, is often acquired but may also, in part, be based on hereditarily established nerve structures (IRM's).

We filmed involuntary hand movements—to which no special signaling value yet attaches—among people in various states of excitation: relatives waiting on railway platforms or at airports, courting couples who had yet to overcome their inhibitions, people who were impatient, hesitant, or angry. The films show hands playing with each other, gripping each other, squeezing and fondling each other. Alternatively, one hand asserts its independence, strays to throat and face, strokes the chin, toys with nose or ears. Fingers scratch the scalp or the corners of the eyes; an individual finger picks the teeth or worries a nostril. From the point of view of behavioral research, these are mainly displacement activities of the kind which animals perform in quite an analogous way. A state of excitation elicits actions which are meaningless in the given context. Very often when a waiting man reaches for a newspaper, lights a cigarette, or orders himself a drink, he really performs these actions for their own sake, not because he has a compulsion to read, smoke, or drink. The human being finds it difficult to behave calmly, especially when he is in a state of conflict.

There are also some movements born of excitation which reveal just what the person in question would really like to do. For example, a priest whom we filmed sitting on a bench in Cuzco, Peru, could not make up his mind whether to remain seated or get up and go. This emerged clearly from our accelerated film, which showed how his body stirred briefly in a series of false starts. We have already discussed the fact that such movements of intent are common among animals. Man provides numerous examples. If a man is hungry, certain movements of the mouth tell us so. If he is enraged or aggressively inclined, he clenches his fists. Because we normally focus our attention on facial movements, with the eyes as our point of focus, we pay little heed to the no less expressive and informative movements of the hands.

One very primitive movement of intent is the slight opening and forward jerk of the hand which occurs when we want to take something. This movement can be observed with particular frequency in children. The palm turns uppermost as if to receive something. It is very probable that this movement formed the origin of the human begging movement, which is used all over the world and is universally understood. The outstretched, upturned palm is an easily understandable signal meaning, "Please give." Beggars simplify it by holding the hand out passively, not that this in any way diminishes the signaling power of the gesture. A film we made of two Negro children showed how the sister instructed her little brother in the art of begging by guiding his hand. This would indicate that the gesture is acquired. It is probable, however, that an innate learning disposition is involved here as well, because the gesture is also used by chimpanzees, our nearest anthropoid relations.

Interestingly enough, chimpanzees perform the gesture in a still more metaphorical sense. With them, as Jane Goodall was able to observe, the begging movement has developed into a request for permission and confirmation. If a low-ranking animal wants to eat a banana when a senior is nearby, the former will extend its paw to the latter with palm upturned. The senior signifies approval by placing its paw, palm downward, on that of the supplicant. Only then will the junior animal venture to take the banana. Jane Goodall observed another use of this signal among female chimpanzees when they introduce their newborn babies—which they bring into the world in solitude—to the group. Very diffidently, the mother takes her baby to the various members of the troop and presents it, extending her paw in just such a gesture of entreaty. She shows no sign of reassurance until she has received the corresponding gesture of approval. The youngster is then formally received into the troop.

Another human gesture which obviously derived from a movement of intent is the raising of the hand as a signal for "Halt! Keep your distance!" This movement clearly conveys an intention to ward something off and may well be hereditarily fixed. The contrary signal for "Come closer"—a beckoning gesture—stems from the intention to gather something in.

Of the forms of greeting Eibl studied, the raising and exposing of the palm is a very primitive signal denoting a friendly attitude. This gesture resembles the signal for "Halt!" but is clearly distinguishable from the latter. In "Halt!" the palm is thrust forward vigorously; in the gesture of salutation the arm is raised calmly and the empty palm exposed as an unmistakable sign that a person is unarmed or has laid his weapon aside—in other words, that he harbors no hostile intentions. As we have already mentioned, similar forms of greeting have evolved among animals. The albatross, for instance, points its beak skyward in greeting—in other words, away from the recipient of the greeting. Ramming a spear into the ground is a human salutation with the same inherent basic meaning, as is the laying aside of weapons before entering a hut. Raising one's hat as a modern form of salutation is derived from doffing the helmet. The military salute is said to have evolved from raising the visor, and presenting arms should probably be construed as a symbolic offering of one's own weapon to another. These last-named forms of salutation arose in a wholly traditional way, as did the raised-fist salute customarily used in Communist countries—a threatening form of salution which symbolizes a united front against a third party.

Folding of the hands is a widespread sign of prayer and, in Siam, a token of greeting. This posture has been interpreted as a ritualized gesture of submission, in that the hands, folded and empty of weapons, are held out for another to bind. Pilgrims whom I photographed at prayer in Banaras raised their folded hands somewhat higher. This recalled the begging movement and might thus have been derived from the intention to take something. Finally, the fingers are sometimes interlocked as well, and the gesture turns into hand wringing. Eibl suggests that this is a ritualized groping for help and quest for protection. Just as the child clings to its mother, so the two hands —lacking anything to grasp—cling to each other. The folding of the hands may therefore stem from a variety of sources.

Other gestures which I recorded among the Hindus are wholly conventional, that is to say, passed on by tradition. Smiting the breast is symbolic of self-chastisement or remorse. Immersion in the sacred water of the Ganges symbolizes purification, as does pouring it over one's head, sprinkling the eyes and other parts of the body with it, and imbibing it. I managed to record an interesting series of scooping movements performed by believers kneeling on the bank. Many of them scooped up water in their hands and raised it to the sky in a gesture of prayer—probably as a sign of worship. Others, also with hollowed palms raised, performed a somewhat less extreme movement which involved touching the water with the backs of the hands only. In still other cases, the gesture had become totally divorced from the water; the upturned palms merely described small rhythmical movements in the air. The development of traditional ritualization can readily be traced here.

Many gestures can depart so far from their original meaning in this way that their origin becomes unidentifiable. When the devout Shintoist claps his hands at prayer in the temple, it is to be assumed that he is seeking to attract God's attention to himself and his requests. When the Hindu praying in the Ganges turns to face each cardinal point of the compass in turn, he is probably addressing himself to the deities that dwell there. When the Christian makes the sign of the cross, on the other hand, it is necessary to know something about an incident that occurred almost 2,000 years ago in order to understand the origin of the movement. Symbolic gestures of this kind have developed into various rituals, and there are similar movements in many dances. They lead on to arbitrarily devised gestures of communication such as deaf-and-dumb language.

One gesture undoubtedly influenced by heredity is the bowing of the head in token of submission. Analogous movements are to be found in many animal appeasement gestures, by means of which an inferior activates the appropriate inhibition in its superior. Either the most vulnerable part of the body is presented—the vanquished wolf exposes its unprotected throat to the victor—or the animal performs the contrary of a threat movement by lying flat on the ground in front of its superior rival. In man there is a combination of both elements: the antithesis of the impressive stance, and the presentation of a particularly vulnerable spot—the unprotected back of the head. Self-observation discloses that this still activates a corresponding inhibition in us today, if only a vague one. Looking as tall as possible and expanding the chest is universally employed by human beings as a means of intimidating an adversary, as witness the behavior of small boys. So long as man's ancestry remained obscure, it was possible to regard this as an unimportant similarity, but it is really a signaling movement with an analogous basis. The same applies to the opposite behavior, our appeasement posture. This, too, developed in the course of time—and through conventional ritualization—into the bow of greeting, which was eventually indicated by no more than a slight nod of the head.

One problem which particularly interested me was the origin of the widespread head signals for yes and no—the nod and the shake. Exceptions occur here, too. The Ceylonese, for example, affirm by means of a rhythmical to-and-fro movement of the head, and we filmed Italians who signified negation by raising their heads and inclining them backward slightly. Darwin assumed that head shaking derives from the movement made by an infant rejecting food, and that our nod—as a clearly opposed signal—originally expressed willingness to accept food (in which case the head is inclined forward). However, our films suggested a somewhat different explanation.

There can be little doubt that head shaking has its origin in the child's gesture of rejection. It is a ritualized turning away to left and right, possibly combined with the shaking-off movement of disgust. The nod for yes, however, seems more likely to be a curtailed inclination of the head—that is to say, a ritualized appeasement gesture. An almost exactly similar nodding movement was visible in our accelerated films of politely bowing Japanese. In the course of human evolutionary history, a change may have occurred similar to the one we viewed with the aid of the artificial distortion of time by the accelerated films. Just as movements of aversion are correspondingly curtailed, accelerated, and reiterated in our "no," so, in the case of "yes," a corresponding curtailment, acceleration, and reiteration may have occurred. By saying yes, one accepts the views, suggestions, or commands of another. This provides the obvious transition.

Shaking the hand as a further sign of negation is also widely found in various races. As Darwin himself suggested, this movement is probably analogous to head shaking. Raising the hand to the mouth is another very primitive gesture, this time of surprise. A surprised man opens his mouth and draws a reflex breath—and his raised hand screens the orifice in an instinctive and quite involuntary movement. Reflex inhalation also occurs in response to shock or fear, and here again the hand displays a similar tendency.

One hand movement, which we filmed in a wide variety of places, is habitually used in speech. This involves placing the tips of thumb and forefinger together to emphasize a line of argument. Usually, the hand moves agitatedly to and fro, and the speaker often concludes the gesture by abruptly baring his open palm at the other party. This generally stresses the speaker's punchline and may be evaluated as the symbolic disclosure of an idea, the proffering of facts. We filmed the same gesture with a Samoan dancer, who performed it with both hands and rhythmically repeated it. However, the basic meaning was probably the same: a symbolic disclosure and proffering of one's own nature, one's own *joie de vivre,* one's own charms.

Another movement often observed in conversation is pointing with the finger—a gesture which the infant already performs at the crawling stage. In its original form, the gesture consists in placing the tip of the forefinger on objects which it is necessary to draw to the attention of others. If such an object is some distance away, the fingertip points in the appropriate direction. In conversation, the speaker points metaphorically to the assertion which he happens to be making, to an objection which he wishes to raise, to a fact which is to be indicated. A finger signal of this kind may also refer to past or future events. The forefinger raised in menacing accusation points warningly to a certain intention. Pointing when issuing an order has a similar significance—or indicates the object of the order. And in Siamese dancing, which is highly ritualized, this sign coupled with a turn of the hand has come to mean a challenge to do battle.

Very primitive forms of gesture were exemplified by films which we took of actors in Europe and Japan. What interested us here, apart from manual gestures, were the no less expressive movements of the head and entire body. The actor has to transmit ideas and emotions for a considerable distance, and for this purpose he exaggerates certain expressive movements which are performed in daily life.

Actresses illustrated the constituents of feminine coquetry

for us with particular clarity. A subtle aversion of the head and body signifies, "I am shy and about to run away." And the backward glance, coupled with an appropriate smile, means, "But I won't object if you follow me." The interplay between these two ritualized elements—shrinking modesty and covert provocation—constitutes a signal stimulus which operates upon a prospective mate. It is as certain that the female does not have to acquire this technique as it is that the male possesses an innate understanding thereof.

Excitation—to return to the starting point of this chapter— leads to many and varied restless movements and is similarly represented on the stage. We found a particularly extreme form of ritualization among the actors of the classical kabuki theater in Tokyo, whose "plays" consist largely of motor patterns established by tradition. The female roles are taken by men.

The kabuki woman—as we shall call this hermaphroditic performer for simplicity's sake—conveys agitation by a slight shaking of the head. This signal tells the audience, "I am excited." But the audience must gauge whether the excitement is pleasurable or distressing from the remainder of the action. The sign for impatience is similar but clearly distinguishable. The entire upper part of the body sways to and fro in a ritualized movement which is as simple as it is effective. I filmed a Samoan woman performing almost exactly the same swaying motion in real life. Classical tradition forbids a Japanese girl to flirt openly. All smiles must be hidden by the hand, and the focus of attention is revealed only by a slight inclination of the head and the direction of the veiled glance. The kabuki woman conveys weeping by shaking her head and wiping away tears with a ritualized gesture similar to one which we found among Siamese dancers. Stamping the foot as a sign of rage is an age-old human gesture derived from the step taken preliminary to an attack. Similar movements are found among animals. The kabuki woman expresses weariness by a highly ritualized gesture: The hand is placed flat against the cheek, and the head inclined and moved gently to and fro. Here the hand symbolizes the pillow on which the head would like to rest, and the movement of the head conveys the actor's impatience at his inability to achieve the desired state. Another ritualized gesture expresses jealousy: The kabuki woman turns her head slightly to one side, places the tip of her scarf in her mouth, bites on it (pulling the scarf downward with both hands at the same time), focuses her gaze on the object of her jealousy, and moves her head back and forth. The act of biting the tip of the scarf represents a redirected minatory movement. The bite is not really directed at the scarf but at an object of hatred.

The kabuki man, by contrast, is not allowed to convey agitation by means of physical movement. Classical tradition enjoins the male Japanese to practice self-control. Here, ritualized lip movements have become the means of communication. When portraying a father whose son has disgraced the family, the performer assumes a majestic pose and stands completely motionless. Only his lips move, twitching in a prescribed manner. Extreme fury is conveyed by parting the lips still farther, baring the eyeteeth, and intensifying the twitch of the lips. Indeed, the whole face begins to twitch and the eyes roll—a permissible sign that the man is losing his self-control entirely. The kabuki man is, however, allowed to portray the convulsive movements of uncontrollable grief quite openly. He does not hide his face until the advent of tears.

As unrehearsed films of daily life showed us yet again, people talking excitedly use many redirected minatory gestures to emphasize aspects of verbal communication. When angry people smite the air they are really smiting the person who has occasioned their anger. A man engaged in fierce argument sometimes grabs the air as a means of holding his listener's attention. Films of South Italians clearly illustrated the transition from direct to redirected movement. If one man wishes to attract another's attention, he often takes him by the sleeve and shakes him or grips him by the shoulder or lapel. This form of physical contact helps to reinforce the transmission of personal intent and is aimed at intimidation. If the speaker does not venture to make such direct contact, the same movements are performed in the air and serve the same purpose—less forcibly but to good effect.

Biologists have long known that the life processes, like inorganic chemical reactions, are accelerated by an increase in temperature. In evolution, this was a prerequisite of the development of warm-blooded creatures—mammals and birds—and of the successful survival of this new "arrangement." Warm-blooded creatures gained ascendancy over the more sluggish cold-blooded creatures, especially in cooler regions. Man compounded this advantage by means of clothing and heated houses, though the Southern races enjoy a quicker life process and generally attain sexual maturity at an earlier age. Comparison of films showing Neapolitans and North Norwegians conversing demonstrated that temperament can be similarly influenced. Accelerated sequences clearly revealed that far fewer "air movements" are performed in the North.

Thus, by-products of states of excitation developed into communication signals in the course of human evolutionary history. If a movement which was meaningless in itself conveyed a certain mood with sufficient clarity, suitable mechanisms of recognition gradually adapted themselves to it, thereby paving the way for its further reinforcement and ritualization. As we said at the outset, lack of order gave birth to a new functional unit—in other words, to something useful to the organism.

The view currently held by most biologists is that much the same applies to the development of physical structures. Changes in hereditary dispositions led to deviations from the norm, and these initially random formations could—if, say, a creature changed its habitat—suddenly acquire meaning. Selection then promoted improvements in these structures, and that is how suitably specialized organs came to be formed.

That which is useful in a living creature is useful only with respect to a function required by the organism. Nothing is useful if it does not contribute to or produce an effect.

14

Man and Multicellular Organism

MORE than 1,200,000 different species of living things (including plants) have now been identified, 500,000 of them insects. Each of these multitudinous forms represents a system for the division of labor, a quite specific arrangement of functional units. Each is capable of doing certain things, the basic object being the same in every case: first, to acquire energy and matter and rebuild them into its specific structure; and second, to keep disruptive or hostile forces at bay.

In order to impose a certain order on this vast multitude and render it easier for our brain to comprehend, scientists have divided living creatures into groups. Linnaeus, the first to tackle this monumental task successfully, proceeded from external and structural similarities. Then, when the theory of evolution—according to which all surviving species are branches of the same great family tree—achieved its breakthrough with Darwin, biologists strove to make this natural relationship the basis of classification; in other words, to group together species which are closely related in terms of evolutionary history. This modified many aspects of the system devised by Linnaeus and brought a "natural system" into being.

The first major step toward classification was to separate the two great animal and vegetable kingdoms. These two groups differ fundamentally in their modes of acquiring energy and matter.

The two kingdoms do, it is true, overlap at the base, so no clear dividing line can be drawn at that level. Many unicellular organisms may be regarded as either animals or plants and are therefore included in their respective systems by zoologists and botanists alike. There are, for instance, minute flagellate organisms which both acquire and assimilate food in animal fashion. The life process split up and evolved an immense number of organizational types in each of these two main fields.

Both animals and plants may be further divided into unicellular and multicellular organisms, but here too the frontier is ill-defined. Types of amoebae exist which remain unicellular for a time and then combine to form extremely complicated multicellular structures (*e.g.,* the mucor). Some flagellate organisms form colonies by normal division, these consisting of sixteen cells which remain firmly united. In the case of others, hundreds of cells form a globule by means of a process which already amounts to a division of labor among individual cells. However, since multicellular organisms are derived from unicellular, it is only natural that such transitional forms should occur. Some of these have continued to reproduce themselves to this day, thus affording us an opportunity, even now, of studying the erstwhile course of evolution.

The zoologist (as opposed to the botanist, who makes no such distinction) divides the kingdom of animal organisms into the two subkingdoms: Protozoa (unicellular) and Metazoa (multicellular). Multicellular organisms are divided according to their main structural characteristics into a further filing system of categories (phyla, classes, orders, families, etc.). For example, the following major phyla are distinguished: Porifera, Coelenterata, Arthropoda, Mollusca, Echinodermata, and Chordata. The last-named phylum is subdivided into several subphyla, of which the mammals are one. One of their constituent orders is that of the primates, and the latter, in turn, includes the species *Homo sapiens,* or man.

Where physical organization is concerned, only minor characteristics distinguish us from the apes. But view man in the light suggested by this book, namely, as a creature which has amplified its physical organization by the addition of artificial organs, and the picture changes. The old form of systematic classification loses its validity.

In man, the life process has attained a superior principle of organization which differs as fundamentally from that of the Metazoa as their principle of organization differs from that of the Protozoa. In man, the life process achieved yet another immensely significant advance. The creature "man" succeeded in supplementing the integral organs built up by his hereditary formula with other organs which need not consist of human tissue and which he can discard, exchange, and even operate by means of energy extraneous to his own body. The same individual can thus transform himself into a variety of organized productive systems. The hunter with his rifle and telescopic sight is quite a different organizational structure from the fisherman who operates with boat and nets. Further development of specialized occupations—which we shall discuss a bit later—produced specialists such as cobblers, lawyers, and dentists, all of whom represent distinct organizational structures.

The naked human frame is only the starting point for the formation of productive systems comprising many more functional units, just as the germ cell of the metazoon is only a starting point for the formation of larger productive systems. Consequently, anyone who adduces this centerpiece alone—the naked human frame—for purposes of comparison and classification is not doing justice to the special nature of the further development that has taken place. It is only the *entire productive body* of the employed person which is comparable to the bodies of organisms.

Functionally, the transition from multicellular creature to human specialist can be very clearly formulated, being dependent upon a decisive functional change. From the bottom of the scale up to the highest multicellular organisms, the hereditary formula has always functioned to develop individual organs. In man, the central nervous system—hitherto responsible only for organic control—took on the additional task of forming more organs whose purposive employment it likewise controlled. So important were the consequences of this functional take-over and the structural changes arising therefrom that it is justifiable to regard human types of organization as radically different from the rest. Given the existence of artificial organs, it is only logical to classify the productive bodies man developed as a third subkingdom on a par with unicellular and multicellular organisms, distinction being drawn between the numerous categories of human occupations. In view of the continuous flowering of the life process, this form of classification seems far more appropriate than one which ignores man's peculiar abilities and simply groups him with the apes—putative ancestors whom he has, where organization is concerned, outstripped by a vast distance.

What of the individual forms of livelihood which have led to man's accretion of power? To be more exact, what of the structure and behavior of these "productive bodies" and their real bases of existence?

This is precisely the question the biologist asks with respect to all other organisms. The central problem is always: How does this beetle or that alga acquire the quantities of energy and matter necessary to its development—that is to say, in the broadest sense, its food? And again: How does our understanding of this central problem help explain the physical organization in question and the behavior peculiar to its species? Applying this form of inquiry to the specialized productive bodies which man constructs in his various forms of occupation, we find the first stage to be very similar to those of animal organisms. The hunter and fisherman are good examples of this. Both forms of specialist are equipped with artificial organs and, equally, with the acquired coordinations needed to employ these organs usefully. The product of their endeavors is as certainly food as it is in the case of any animal, except that these human beings succeed in considerably increasing their yield and reducing their exertions by the specialized amplification of their bodies.

The second stage comprises forms of livelihood in which human intelligence finds still clearer expression, e.g., agriculture. In the natural state, each area can normally support only a limited number of individuals of a certain organizational type —in other words, of a particular species of animal or plant. Our ancestors, apes and primeval men, were just as affected by this limitation as any other living creature. Apes lived on fruit, parts of plants, and smaller animals; primitive man extended his hunting activities to larger beasts. Although the idea of refraining from eliminating all edible plants in a given area and of artificially cultivating plants suitable for food seems quite logical to us today, it actually represented a truly gigantic step forward, because the same area could support many more individuals in this way. Precisely the same factors applied to cattle breeding. Far more quarry could be raised on the same ground, and the difficulties of hunting diminished.

This was not, however, the greatest advance of all. As we saw, man succeeded in forming far larger communities than accorded with his hereditary disposition to live in groups. These larger groups evolved a division of labor whereby individuals could specialize in different pursuits. Because of the importance attained by artificial organs, it happened in the course of time that some members of the community specialized in their manufacture. Food could now be acquired by bartering these products. This, too, seems obvious today. In fact, it presupposes a feat of intelligence which demands closer scrutiny.

Agriculture itself demanded an ability to relate causes and effects separated by more than half a year. This feat of intelligence consisted in grasping that activities which brought no immediate return—clearing ground, digging, etc.—could very well produce food at a later point in time. It was exactly the same with cattle breeding. Here, man had to grasp that *not* killing an animal could lead to the acquisition of *more* food—on the face of it, a paradoxical notion. Such is the essential feat of intelligence of which the ape's brain is incapable. It can relate causes and effects, but only when these are in close temporal and spatial conjunction. When we come to the acquisition of food by the manufacture of artificial organs, the occupational relationship becomes considerably more complicated still. In the case of a swordsmith, for instance, none of his occupational movements led to the acquisition of animals or plants, yet his activities brought him food. The connection between cause and effect has here been rendered still more obscure by an intermediate factor. Experiments conducted with chimpanzees by Yerkes and Wolfe have shown that apes, too, can be made to grasp such an indirect connection. They cannot, however, produce the connection by themselves.

Human barter did not become really fruitful until the further invention of money. Only this neutral medium—itself an artificial organ—made it possible to convert any one form of output into any other and, if need be, acquire the yield of *several* forms of output by other people in exchange for *one* such form of output by onself.

A need for other people thus became the essential basis of such human occupations. Individual human productive bodies are just as much adapted in structure and behavior to this need —which we generally refer to as the market—as animals are to their sources of food. And just as the emergence of each new animal species became, in turn, a basis for the existence of other species (as a potential source of food), so every new form of occupation in the human economy became a basis for the existence of others. Again, just as each area can support only so many members of an animal or vegetable species, so each rural district or urban quarter can support only a limited number of doctors, shoemakers, or grocers. Thus, although outwardly very different from animal and vegetable organisms, human productive bodies are subject to similar laws. The first point of difference is that their parts are not firmly integrated and that they can therefore grow far more freely than organisms. Their artificial organs can be renewed as required. "Reproduction" follows quite a different and far simpler course, and it is even possible for one productive body to transform itself into another. On the other hand, the competition between productive bodies which strive to exploit the same source of livelihood is just as fierce. And, once again, a process of natural selection ensures that the most efficient bodies prevail.

What complicates the picture is that man uses artificial organs not merely for productive purposes but also for the attainment of pleasure. This human tendency, of which we shall have more to say later, is a further manifestation of our intelligence and progress. Animals and plants cannot employ the product of their exertions for anything but structural growth or multiplication, but man is not so constrained. He can use his surplus production to procure pleasure, and for that purpose he has created countless other artificial organs which clothe him like a gorgeous and resplendent robe. However, what exclusively determines the existence and advancement of the individual is his *acquired* structure, which must therefore be enlisted in any account and definition of these special organizational forms of the life process. This structure invariably consists, first, of the employed person himself, and second, of the totality of the artificial organs requisite to his form of productive activity, whether these be owned by the person or merely hired by him or communally available within the framework of an existing community. Third, the structure must also embody all the control formulas necessary to a particular form of occupation. These are present in the brain of the person but may exist partly in the shape of artificial organs (plans, manuals, etc.).

Through the medium of man, the life process attained a still greater expansion of power and the formation of still more complex structures. Various people with manifold artificial organs banded themselves together, as we have shown, into even more highly integrated bodies—hence the existence of firms, factories, and other productive organizations. In these, man himself assumes the role of a mere organ, and many of his functions may be just as well performed by an artificially created structure (machine, apparatus). If we apply the same criterion to these types of organizations, too, they represent yet another organic subkingdom—the fourth.

These productive organizations, to employ my proposed term for this new category, may be constructed wholly or partly of other organizations (as in the case of a financial trust or political system). This does not, however, create a need for more basic distinctions. However intricate the process becomes, no new principle of organization will emerge. An organization which forms part of another is just as much an organ of the same as a man or machine. It is no more than a functional unit, a performer of very specific tasks within the work-sharing system. Hence, this group contains all independently operating *superindividual* productive bodies including political systems —insofar as these represent organizations which promote increased production. By contrast, a system of government which confines its functions to external defense and the maintenance of internal order is a communal organ belonging to its citizens.

There is no clear line of demarcation between the third sub-kingdom of occupations and the fourth subkingdom of productive organizations. If an employed person—a shoemaker, say —employs assistants, these constitute artificial organs within the morphological structure of his occupational body. Once his business expands into an industrial footwear-manufacturing concern, it becomes a superindividual productive body—a superindividual organization. It is immaterial how the proceeds are divided up, whether one man bears the risks and reaps the profits, or whether a group of people hold shares in the organization. What matters is the superindividuality which transforms even a proprietor into an organizational—and replaceable —component. This superindividuality constitutes a special factor which justifies the isolation of a fourth subkingdom. Like all classifications of the natural system, this is an artificial classification which we impose on nature for the sake of easier supervision and better understanding, so we should not be worried by the absence of clear definition. In practice, an employed person whose artificial organs include human assistants will continue to be classified in the third subkingdom for as long as he himself is the genuinely dominant productive component. If more and more specialists join a productive body until each of them, including the central organizer, produces only a limited share of the total output, this turns the organization into a different and more highly integrated productive system.

The transition from multicellular organism to human specialist is considerably clearer. Not only does it follow from the assumption of organic development by the central nervous system, which we have already discussed, but it is characterized by another and no less important functional change. Each evolutionary advance—each specific mutation—made by every multicellular organism had always been governed by the hereditary formula. Only changes in that formula could lead to hereditary modifications and improvements. One institution which promoted such improvements was the coupling of the sexes. By this means, hereditary formulas were mingled and random hereditary changes (arising from mutations) were permuted ad infinitum. This increased the likelihood that a more efficient structure would take shape. The organizational type "man" now underwent an important change in that his central nervous system assumed the function of a promoter of evolution. Thanks to our intelligence, we human beings improved ourselves. Having succeeded in improving our bodies, we passed on the formulas for newly developed structures to others—and what is more, directly (via speech and writing). From then on, the whole laborious system of mingling hereditary factors by means of the sexual act became obsolete. The tempo of potential improvement—in the sense of adaptation and accretion of power—was accelerated a hundred thousandfold. Where multicellular organisms were concerned, the way had been paved for this development among the learners when their central nervous system increasingly assumed the task of creating behavioral formulas. In man, a stage was suddenly reached where the central nervous system intervened in the matter of physical development and improvement. It planned the construction and linkage of supplementary functional units, supervised their testing and manufacture, and assumed responsibility for passing on formulas for their construction and use. It now became possible to pass on physical structures created by experience as well. Even the need for *active* procreation—hitherto an inseparable feature of the life process—was now superseded. Productive bodies formed by men may also be *copied* by other men, so that a productive body can reproduce itself without the slightest expenditure of effort. The dividing line between the numerous organizational types represented among multicellular organisms and the far more successful productive bodies constituted by human specialists and productive organizations is thus very distinct; it is characterized by several basic functional changes. Only our body itself remained within the competence of the hereditary formula. That which constitutes our real physical peculiarity, on the other hand, became the responsibility of the central nervous system.

The term "species" was originally governed by the criterion of sexual compatibility. Individual creatures were ascribed to the same species if they could mate and produce fertile offspring. Difficulties later arose in the case of many classifications,

The young human being has the same innate curiosity drive as the young of the higher vertebrates: an Indian child in Cuzco exploring his surroundings as well as testing his own behavior and resulting reactions. This is how, impelled by instinct, the child builds up the behavioral controls necessary for existence; in other words, he "learns."

Parents have an innate urge to teach their offspring. Learning by imitation is an intellectual feat of which, apart from man, only the highest vertebrates (*e.g.,* monkeys, wolves, cats) are capable. Demonstration and imitation form the basis of human development, both drives being innate in us.

One of the loneliest villages in the world is Molo on Lake Rudolf in Uganda. Like children everywhere, the local youngsters play "building houses." Such is the power of human imagination that a few bent palm fronds suffice to symbolize a house. The children enjoy the shade and invite their friends inside.

The reflex intake of breath in response to a surprise is an innate reaction which prepares the human body for defensive measures. Simultaneously —another reflex action—the hand darts to the mouth. We filmed this fixed-action pattern in various races (Karamoja woman, Frenchwoman). It is identical everywhere.

The reflex repulsion of an approaching body became, by process of ritualization, the innate signal for "Keep away!" Throughout the world, as seen in the second photograph, the calmly raised hand has acquired the traditional meaning: "I am unarmed and well disposed toward you!" The third photograph shows an individual hand signal: "Strictly between ourselves. . . ."

The movement denoting an intention to grasp something has become the traditional and universally understood signal for "Give me!" Progressive ritualization is evident in the second photograph: The same message is conveyed by an open palm passively extended (blind beggar). The signal has greater impact in a little child, which is why in the third photograph the elder child is using the younger's hand.

The movement denoting an intention to touch something with one's finger became the signal for "There!" We point to our heads when wishing to draw attention to an idea. We may also, in conversation, point to something quite abstract, *e.g.,* an argument. In Siamese dancing, further abstraction has transformed the act of pointing into a challenge to mortal combat.

Hindus praying beside the Ganges: A scooping movement symbolizes the raising of sacred water to the Deity. The pilgrim in the second photograph, while making the same movement, barely touches the water. In the third photograph the gesture has become entirely divorced from its original medium. *Opposite:* Ritual movements whose origin almost defies elucidation.

This bear used to live in a smaller enclosure, which is why it still shuttles to and fro between invisible boundaries when moved to a larger one. Similarly, on the opposite page, speeded-up films showed that the news vendor spent his entire day shuttling between the same sections of building walls. This stereotyped behavior arises from man's innate desire to protect his rear.

The inability to satisfy urges or desires tends to "bottle up" excitation, and this—in man as in animals—results in "displacement activities." Scratching and picking the nose or teeth—even smoking and drinking—may then act purely as safety valves. This is another innate and universal form of behavior.

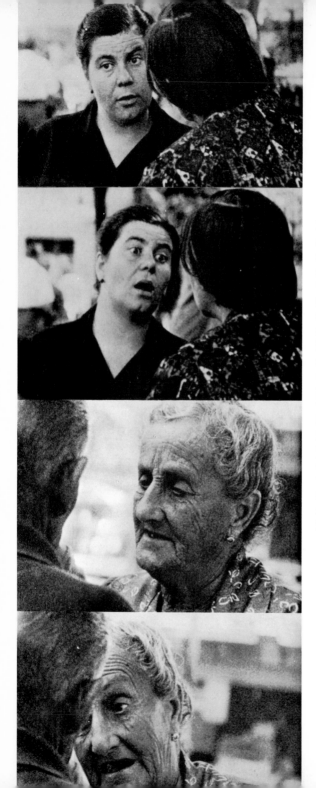

It is possible not onl suppress hereditarily f modes of behavior conscious effort but to intensify and even nipulate them. All r convey surprise by ening the eyes and ing the eyebrows—ar nate movement not quired by learning. M people (like these Ita women) intensify fixed-action pattern further in order to phasize a statement w conversing. The stim tive effect of an in signal is thus artific reinforced. Whether not the surprise rem "genuine" is an (question. It may be pu simulated.

ning the mouth is a
ersal sign of curiosity.
South American In-
girl in our first pic-
is giving an involun-
performance of this
te movement. The
e other pictures show
Italian listening in-
ly to another. His
th, too, is open—in
our film showed that
mained so for more
a minute. This is
ably another instance
which an expression
genuine curiosity has
enerated into a con-
tional mark of cour-
denoting interest on
part of the listener.

When an actress of the Kabuki Theater in Tokyo bites the end of her sleeve and wags her head to and fro, the audience knows she is jealous. In this case, both performer and behavior are artificial products. Understanding of the gesture depends on tradition, and the actress is really a man.

and it was decided to group as a species those related creatures which conform in basic structural characteristics. The system of classifying productive bodies evolved by the life process advanced in the foregoing chapter takes this mode of observation a stage further. Because the life process has superseded both sexuality and the need for active procreation, it is no longer justifiable to define the structural types attained by the life process essentially in terms of these characteristics. To do so may still serve a purpose up to the level of the apes, but there is a radical change in premises from the human specialist onward. At this level, the species can be defined only as a spatio-temporal order which possesses viability and, thus, expediency with respect to a certain environmental situation. The term "species," like many other human concepts, is a man-made category artificially erected in the midst of nature. Demarcation thus has practical value alone and is not by any means a natural phenomenon.

15

Imprinting and Freedom

As master of this planet, man today faces two major problems. First, how is he to avoid annihilating himself with his ever more efficient weapons and create a universal order which will bring justice and a fair share of the world's goods to all? Second, what practical use should he make of his dominant position, his life, his opportunities; what line should he take, and to what values should he ultimately subordinate himself?

Each of these problems poses a third, which must be resolved first of all. Briefly, we must ask ourselves if it is actually possible for us to "want what we want." A marionette moves because it is worked by strings. Metaphorically speaking, animals are often worked by strings in that the courses of their existences are largely dictated by certain of the nerve structures built up by their hereditary formulas. We human beings are vastly superior to animals in our unique capacity to observe and pass judgment on ourselves. But what of our own freedom of action? Do we, too, dangle from invisible strings, and if so, what form do these strings take?

There is, first, the long period during which man approaches maturity and acquires the abilities he needs for life. Our cousins, the higher vertebrates, who likewise come into the world "incomplete," pass through certain sensitive periods which finally determine their subsequent behavior. A structure takes shape in their brain which determines certain actions and reactions for the rest of their lives. If the gosling sees a blue balloon instead of its mother during the first few days of existence, it will follow a blue balloon—exclusively and with implicit obedience—from then onward. If a young cockerel is imprinted with ducks during its sensitive sexual period, it will be indifferent to hens for the rest of its days and strut into the water to court ducks. And if the young nightingale is imprinted with the song of the blackcap, it will, when its own capacity for song matures, sing like a blackcap. Do similar phenomena exist in man?

During its first weeks of life, a child is receptive to few sensory impressions. Although the eyes are quite well developed, the brain is incapable of processing the messages they send. The child is scarcely aware of its own mother during this period. Innate norms of action and reaction ensure that it can find the breast and suck, but it sleeps for more than twenty hours in twenty-four. Not until the second month does it gradually begin to "awaken." Its first act of comprehension is effected—as the original meaning of the word implies—with the hands. At this period the child begins to recognize its mother and distinguish her from other people. It learns—in the natural course of events—that this component of its environment is friendly and solicitous, that it bestows protection, comfort, and nourishment, and that reliably predictable responses can be elicited from it by appropriate behavior. This is the period when the child develops a positive fundamental attitude toward life and environment which Erikson has termed "basic trust."

This basic trust constitutes a pillar of the human personality. If it does not take shape at this stage, it obviously cannot be acquired later. Experiments conducted in nurseries and orphanages have shown that the second half-year of life is crucial to the formation of basic trust. During this period the child requires a measure of personal contact which will promote a sense of security. People who say that a child needs love are right, but only partly. The truth of the matter is that a child needs a partner to whom it can attach itself emotionally. Inmates of children's homes lack this personal relationship. Members of the staff change jobs or go on vacation, thereby rupturing a contact. This has a traumatic effect on some children. As Spitz and Bowlby ascertained, they eventually abandon their quest for contacts and subside into apathy—indeed, death occurs in some cases. A substantial number later exhibit grave mental disorders which are almost impossible to eradicate. Basic mistrust has taken the place of basic trust. Petting, fondling, and caressing are not, therefore, a luxury which one bestows on a child but a stimulus situation for which the child has a positive need. If a child loses its parents, it is of crucial importance that a surrogate should be found as quickly as possible. The mother is the natural partner, but another person is equally capable of giving the child what it needs at this juncture.

With most primitive peoples—but also among some civilized races such as the Japanese—mothers carry their babies slung on their backs in a carrier. Children carried in this way seldom cry, and then only when put down. This is a natural and probably innate reaction which has its roots in our remote past. If the child of primitive man lost contact with its mother, it was exposed to attack by predators. Cries, which functioned as a request to the mother to reestablish contact, were thus of species-preserving importance. The young monkey is also carried about by its mother and possesses in its prehensile reflex an excellent means of clinging to the mother's fur immediately after birth. The same reflex is still observable in the human baby. If the hands of a newborn child are brought into contact with a taut clothesline, it will cling with such tenacity that it can support its own weight.

In America, Europe, and other civilized parts of the world, infants are deposited in a cradle or baby carriage—and cry frequently. This crying is natural, under the circumstances, and need not be a symptom of illness or bodily discomfort. A bottle or a pacifier is a suitable and expedient device in this respect. It is, in the truest sense, a dummy surrogate for the mother's breast which simulates maternal proximity for the benefit of an innate mechanism in the child's brain. Rocking has the same effect, though the effect is stronger if the child is supported on the arm. It is popularly said that leaving a child to cry occasionally does no great harm to the child. This may be true.

Eibl's theory is that the American and European's more critical and independent basic outlook on life stems at least in part from the fact that American and European children are generally reared partly isolated from the mother from an early age. A moderate attenuation of basic trust may thus help one cope with the problems of contemporary life.

Next, the child proceeds to crawl and explore its immediate surroundings. Once again, tactile comprehension precedes the far more difficult visual evaluation of environment. The nature of material objects is tested with the hands. At first everything is conveyed to the mouth. Some time later comes the ability to investigate things by means of repeated exploratory "attacks." Each material object has to run the gauntlet of all the senses. The child gains experience with his environment and an insight into the relationship between cause and effect. The first games are of a destructive nature. The child overturns things, tears them, dismembers them, smashes them. Parents who consider such behavior to be negative and punish a child for indulging in it, are mistaken. Not only is it innate and clearly present in all children, but it enables the growing youngster to gain experience with the properties of the material in question. Such action is a natural prelude to the constructive games that come later. Overturning, tearing, dismembering, smashing, and dirtying things are sources of vital and fundamental experience.

The third half-year of life is often marked by a sudden transition to the constructive game. The tower of bricks the mother erects is no longer knocked down. Instead, the child starts to arrange bricks in accordance with its own desires and may even erect small structures. A phase of intensified experimentation sets in, coupled with greater deliberation. Hand in hand with this comes the growth of a capacity for contemplative enjoyment. The child derives pleasure from examining a picture, from the sound of a musical toy it operates itself. The truly human element now begins to unfold. The child starts to experience things and mold them—and derives pleasure from so doing. Intent on training their charges to be orderly, nursery-school teachers often make them dismantle their half-finished "buildings" at the end of a day and stow the pieces away neatly. At such an age, this is wrong. The child has just begun to set its first objectives and should be allowed to pursue them to the end. Most child psychologists consider that the child's later attitude toward work is decisively influenced at this stage. If a child is prevented from pursuing constructive games, this may later result in an unwillingness or inability to carry out tasks consistently and effectively.

Experimentation with material objects is accompanied by experimentation with personal mobility. Having learned to walk in response to an innate urge, the child proceeds to try its hand at climbing, hopping, balancing, standing on one leg, and so on. As with the young of other learners, every conceivable movement is tested and the knowledge of the ability stored. In this respect, girls have an innate penchant for dolls, boys for climbing, wrestling, and hunting games. Both sexes build "houses" and play "families." Not too long ago parents tried to instill a maximum of decorum into their children and did their utmost to prevent them from coming into contact with dirt, let alone danger. This has since been recognized as a mistaken policy. Playing is a form of preparation for life, and too many restrictions can thwart the growth of the initiative which is so important in later years.

No less important are the defiant spells which parents find so disagreeable. Today's view is that these coincide with phases of accelerated growth. By about the beginning of its third year, the child discovers the strength of its willpower and starts to experiment with it. It opposes parental injunctions and thus tests the possible consequences of saying no. Similar periods occur later, at about five and twelve years of age. All these phases are essential to character formation, because this is when the individual and independent will takes shape. The best parental policy at this stage is to steer a middle course between being too strict and being too indulgent. In order to develop properly, a child must learn to subordinate as well as to assert itself. During defiant spells the child deliberately courts opposition and strives to discover how far it can go before encountering a veto. If this veto is not forthcoming, the disorders in later life can be just as serious as if a child were starved of the approval which helps develop its personal and egoistic will.

Freud, whose great merit it was to have recognized the importance of these critical phases in child development, christened the particularly important period bounded by the third and fifth years of life the Oedipal period. It is during this phase that a child's subsequent sexual behavior is decisively influenced—indeed, determined. The child now shows a willingness to identify with its later sexual role and uses its parents as practice aids for subsequent partnership behavior. The boy becomes particularly clinging and affectionate toward his mother, modeling himself upon his father. The girl flirts with her father, thus assuming the mother's role. If the parental partner is insufficiently or excessively responsive, this can—as psychoanalysts have proved in numerous instances—lead to grave disorders in later sexual behavior. It is, however, just as traumatic if the child cannot identify with the parental partner of its own sex. If the mother constantly bemoans a woman's lot, the daughter may become imprinted with a false sexual role. If the father is a chronic drunkard, the son may be afflicted with identificational disorders. To the psychoanalyst, male and female homosexuality is largely rooted in experiences undergone during this period. This signifies nothing more or less than that parents largely determine their children's later sexual behavior by their own behavior.

An even more critical phase, especially for boys, begins during the ninth year of life and continues throughout puberty. This is when the growing human being emerges from the immediate family circle and seeks contact with society at large. He now develops a readiness to adopt patriotic, religious, and ideological positions and looks around for people on whom to model himself. This phase determines whether a person accepts or rejects the ethical concepts of the society in which he has grown up. The strength of the fixations formed during this phase can be gauged in people who have been educated with a strong ideological bias. In later life—even in the face of contrary experience—they normally find it difficult if not impossible to disregard basic concepts inculcated in them in their youth. Girls are less affected by this development because, in accordance with their biological role as future mothers, they remain more strongly oriented toward the family group. In the man, by contrast, a firm consolidation of beliefs which influence and, indeed, restrict his later judgments now takes place. These beliefs provide the basis on which his later value judgments are made.

Are these steps which take place during a child's development the same as or similar to the phenomenon of animal imprinting? Both Hess and Lorenz, who laid down the exact criteria for animal imprinting, regard the "irreversibilty" of this process as a determining characteristic. The behavioral student accordingly applies the term "imprinting" only to those fixations which cannot be altered during the animal's subsequent life—which are, in fact, irreversible. Biological research has determined, however, that the life process seldom admits sharply defined terms and is full of transitions and exceptions. It may, therefore, eventually be proven that irreversibility is not unalterable in animals either.

The extent to which such fixations are, or are not, irreversible in human beings has not yet been sufficiently explored. Grave disorders in the realm of basic trust, the development of initiative and willpower, and sexual behavior may truly be beyond hope of complete correction. Considering our peculiar capacity for building behavioral formulas and curbing our instincts, it is nevertheless probable that we can combat the effects of such fixations to a degree—in other words, that these are not fundamentally irreversible in man. As a method of therapy, psychoanalysis ultimately stands or falls on its claim to be able, after the event, to remove mental abnormalities developed during childhood.

Thus, whether we refer to this process in man as imprinting or prefer—considering the ethological delimitation of the term —to use some other label is more of an academic and secondary problem. What is certain is that animal learners and human beings alike pass through developmental periods in which the individual seeks certain combinations of stimuli, and that a behavioral structure takes shape according to whether or not these are present. Freud and his pupils discovered these critical periods at a time when virtually nothing was known of animal imprinting, and animal imprinting was discovered quite independently of psychoanalysis. If, despite this, analogous results have been obtained in both fields of research, it strongly suggests that at the very least a close relationship exists between the phenomena that occur in both man and beast.

The first answer to the question "Is it possible for us to want what we want?" therefore goes as follows: That which we describe as our wants, in the broadest sense, is substantially influenced by processes which occur during childhood. Just as a human being's behavior is necessarily impaired by a defective hand, heart, or other organ, so the malformation of certain motor-control structures results in corresponding limitations. The performance of certain actions is inhibited, decisions are restricted in advance, reactions channeled in a predetermined direction. Each of the innumerable control formulas which the brain reconstructs again and again for every action undertaken in life takes shape within a fixed organizational framework. Once this framework is destroyed, the construction of even the simplest formulas may be impaired, thereby affecting each successive judgment, decision, and movement. Thus, one prerequisite of basic human freedom is an unimpaired cerebral apparatus which has developed in a certain way.

Important consequences stem from this. The first and most obvious is that parents should be taught about these sensitive periods in their children's development. The importance of further research in this field need hardly be stressed. If the growth of important behavioral structures is dependent upon essentially trivial and, thus, easily created environmental situations, it obviously is important to investigate these conditions. On the basis of clinical experience, most psychoanalysts go even further in their theories as to what can be destroyed during development in early childhood than I have related here.

Considerable attention has been paid to these views in the United States. It is doubtful if mothers in any other country have been as well instructed by their educational advisers. This makes it doubly important to point out that the United States accords widespread recognition to a concept of upbringing which is incompatible with the results of behavioral research.

In *Frustration and Aggression*, published in 1939, the psychoanalysts Dollard, Miller, Doob, Mowrer, and Sears advanced the theory that all instances of aggression are the result of frustration; that aggressive tendencies and acts directed against fellowmen always stem from the inhibiting or thwarting of some wish or action. The natural corollary of this doctrine is that "evil" human tendencies can be eliminated by eliminating their cause, namely, frustration. Applied to upbringing, this would mean that parents can make their children good-natured and nonaggressive by avoiding frustrating them—in other words, by not preventing the fulfillment of their wishes. By and large people take far more notice of children in the United States than in Europe. Youngsters are thwarted as little as possible for fear of producing frustrations and the mental disorders to which they automatically give rise. Although Dollard and his associates were in the tradition of Freud, their theory tended to conflict with Freudian doctrine. Freud regarded aggression as a wholly autochthonous urge and espoused the view that urges ought to work themselves out.

The frustration theory quickly gained ground and was widely applied, probably because it accorded so well with existing ideas. The Americans, who had always ranked liberty high among their ideals, made it a maxim of child education as well. By the turn of the century Stanley Hall was already advocating greater freedom in childhood, a trend which John Dewey, another prominent educationist, carried much further. Children had to be allowed self-expression—a chance to develop their personalities with the minimum of restraint. The theory put forward by Dollard and his associates fit in with this trend admirably and was also in step with the dogma of the influential behaviorist school of psychology, which rejects the existence of innate urges and holds that practically all human behavior is the product of upbringing. If the frustration theory were correct, the widespread application of permissive methods of upbringing and education in the United States should have caused aggression to decline. Nevertheless, where crimes of violence are concerned, the United States certainly does not lag behind the average European country, and in their professional lives the Americans display a toughness and ruthlessness which Europeans find remarkable.

Behavioral research indicates that aggression in animals is not solely a product of environmental stimuli but a genuine instinct which cannot be unlearned. Everything suggests that this also applies to man. Like every instinct, this one may be blunted—but not eliminated—by diminished indulgence. To avoid crossing a child under any circumstances can only produce unsatisfactory results. From another angle, it is, as we have shown, a mistake because the child has just as much need of an opposing "no"—in other words, *it needs frustration*. Only frustration can prepare it for the restrictions which the framework of human society later imposes on it. Without such opposition the child lacks a stimulus situation which is just as important to its development as the opportunity to express its own will. Since neuroses appear commoner in the United States than elsewhere, it may not be untenably speculative to associate this phenomenon with American methods of upbringing.

A further consequence of imprintinglike processes in man is the vexed problem of whether it is right to imprint a child with subjective ethical concepts and value judgments during the appropriate sensitive period. Is it fair to a developing human being to build up cerebral structures which will later inhibit or obstruct the formation of its own will?

Every human society before our own has been convinced of the rightness of its own approach to life, so it was completely natural for parents and educators to imprint children with the then-prevalent basic moral attitudes—patriotic and religious concepts as well as class and party attitudes. Considering the very changed conditions which prevail today—with special regard to the increased dangers of modern warfare—some rethinking is indicated here. Parents and state alike would do better to refrain from building up cerebral structures in children which will later bring them into conflict.

To be fair to children, one should probably ground them, from the age of six onward, only in those moral concepts which are everywhere the same. They should be warned of the dangers of premature fixation and made to understand that they have an inalienable right to form judgments—a right which they will one day exercise for themselves, perhaps in opposition to their parents and the community. This is a utopian concept at present, but it is possible that just such a trend is already perceptible in today's youth. At least a passion for guitar players or pop singers does not give rise to fixations which may bring subsequent disaster. Thus even the discredited beatniks and their successors have a positive side. The older generation still have an implicit belief that children are more or less a prerogative of theirs and that their own ideals should live on in them. To summon up the courage to ignore the ideals of the older generation is in itself a sign of self-development which should not be underestimated.

This brings us to a third consequence. If our humanity is to develop further, we shall probably have to refrain completely from regarding children as an unlimited personal prerogative. It is remarkable that moral doctrines, religions included, have up to now concerned themselves almost exclusively with safeguarding the fruit of sexual intercourse—the child—while bestowing virtually no thought on how to prevent its unwanted arrival. Imprintinglike processes in man indicate how very important it is for a child to grow up under more or less normal conditions. Thus the idea that it is better for a child to come into the world under any circumstances, rather than remain unborn, also merits reexamination.

Among animals, specific survival depends upon maximal procreation—hence the direction of their instinctive urges. This has also been true of man up to the present, and many communities have actively encouraged the production of as many offspring as possible. Today, thanks yet again to our increased knowledge, we have reached a point where the birthrate is becoming catastrophic and will have to be controlled within the next half-century or so. Given this situation, it is reasonable to suggest that it is not the prevention of unwanted births which must be discouraged but the sanctification of every conceivable human whim. It is illogical to solicit sympathy for starving children instead of penalizing parents for having caused the situation.

The idea of limiting the birthrate by imposing fines—and, eventually, by sterilization—may still seem an intrusion into the rights of the family which is incompatible with human dignity. But has the general attitude which has prevailed up to now been genuinely moral? Is it really compatible with human dignity? If we consider ourselves special and superior beings—which we have every right to do—should responsibility for the existence of a human being be left to the random effects of an emotional condition? Our oftquoted observer from another planet, being unaffected by human emotional fixations, would probably take an entirely different view. He would no doubt see us as more deeply rooted in our animal past in this respect than in any other.

The idea that each individual and marriage is entitled to an average of two children will have to become part of our basic moral code—and only if there is a reasonable willingness and ability to offer those children the conditions they require for proper development. The notion of an arbitrary right to beget children will have to give way to the concept of responsibility and obligation. Man must here learn to separate two things which do not, in themselves, bear the least mutual relationship.

Until the advent of man, the sole function of the sexual urge in the animal world was to produce sufficient offspring. Man now displays a sexual behavior which is not restricted to a particular season of the year but has a continuous effect on his life. Because many domestic animals exhibit a similar hypertrophy, man's excessive sexuality used to be construed as a product of self-domestication and, thus, a rather negative phenomenon. This approach has since been superseded by the theory that human sexuality has acquired another quite distinct function, namely, that of aiding a bond formation. In view of the peculiarly long brood-tending period required by the young of our species it was of great importance to early man that parents should maintain a close protective partnership. The pleasurable sensations occasioned by the sexual act were, so to speak, a mutual incentive to the partners to remain together. Since this second function did not interfere with the first and even promoted it, no complications arose. Multiplied sexual acts reinforced the bond and simultaneously produced a larger number of children. Major evolutionary changes have occurred since then, and we have now reached the stage where one function interferes with the other. Medical progress ensures that too many children survive, and for the first time in evolutionary history procreation is threatening to endanger the existence of a species.

For this reason, it may now be time for us to divorce the problem of procreation from that of sexuality. Our pronounced sexual urge is a legacy which must be coped with, and one to which we owe much more than an enhancement of sensual pleasure. It is probable that many of the greatest human achievements, and the flowering of art in particular, are influenced by this motive force. The making of a new human being, on the other hand, is an act which brings immense responsibilities in its train. The higher man rates himself, the higher he must necessarily rate this process. That is why it should no longer be left to chance and whim, and why any method of separating the two functions of sexuality merits support. As long as the world remained ignorant of imprinting, it was possible to contend that a starving and unloved child was better off alive than unborn. However, our sense of values ought surely to apply to children themselves. Entirely in their interests, we should ensure that no mental cripples come into the world in the first place.

16

Man and Society

To what extent is man the product of his evolutionary past, and to what extent the product of history?

Every species of animal and plant alive today seems to the observer to be a finished unit or "construction." This apparent totality is, however, merely a momentary stage in an evolutionary flow. Just as a succession of tributaries joins together to form a river, so animal and vegetable bodies develop a succession of new structural features which, in turn, develop and improve their various organs.

The origins of each individual organ thus go back varying distances into the past. The eyes of a salamander, for example, are much more ancient in evolutionary terms than its legs. Its ancestors, the fish, already possessed eyes, but legs did not develop until some of those ancestors became land dwellers. Again in terms of evolutionary history, the roots of a rosebush are far older than its flowers: Multicellular plants developed organic aids to stability and nourishment relatively soon after their conquest of terra firma, whereas their flowers developed only in adaptation to the insects that arrived on the scene much later. In the same way, every innate animal behavior pattern has its own date of origin. Every instinct-producing structure, every hereditary disposition and every innate recognition mechanism came into being at some point in the evolutionary flow, and these functional units proceeded to adapt themselves to the work-sharing system operated by the other organs.

The same pattern is visible with the human body and with our own innate behavior patterns. At some point in our ancestors' evolutionary chain our hereditary formula succeeded in building these diverse structures. Each arrived at a particular point and has its own history. Consider our teeth, for example. Comparative research has indicated quite precisely the ancestors to which we "owe" them and how they came into being. They originated more than 300,000,000 years ago, in ancestors from whom the modern shark is also descended. In their case, as in that of the modern shark, the body scales along the edge of the mouth grew longer, forming rows of teeth. In other words, a functional change occurred. From these common ancestors developed the Osteichthyes, or bony fish, and from these, in turn, vertebrate land animals. The body scales eventually disappeared in the course of evolution, but the scales used as teeth survived and underwent gradual modification and improvement. The development of the human embryo still betrays the teeth's origin, and we can still observe the process of organic development through functional change in sharks: Even today, their teeth are really overdeveloped body scales.

On the other hand, the history of those characteristics which constitute our real human peculiarity is entirely different, for they developed quite independently of our hereditary formula. All acquired components of human behavior and all our modern artificial organs were sometime, somewhere, evolved by human beings. Having evolved or been invented, they were handed down by imitation, speech, or writing, via thousands of human brains, to us. Each of these functional units dates from a specific period and has its own history, therefore, but the route by which they reached us varies greatly.

Few people are aware of to what extent each of us is the product of human society. We are born into the world, our consciousness unfolds, and we greet what we see around us as a given factor from which our ego stands divorced, as it were. We are barely conscious of the extent to which this ego is influenced and molded by human society. A human being raised in total isolation—if such a thing were possible—would be capable of only very limited thought processes. That which is peculiar to us takes shape by way of speech and contact with other people, with human experience. With animals and plants, studying isolated individuals makes it possible to analyze the special features of the species in question: the mode of existence for which the structure is equipped, the way it grows and multiplies, how it safeguards and defends itself against disruptive and hostile forces. An observer from another planet could not form similar conclusions with man. Observing a shoemaker would tell him nothing about a dentist's activities. If he studied the social practices of one area, he could make only very limited inferences about other places, however close by. The individual's brain absorbs this or that behavioral formula through contact with society, and it is this which accounts for his particular mode of existence: the artificial functional units he uses for the extension of his body, the form of livelihood he pursues, and to what "orders" he subordinates himself. Behavior determined by the hereditary formula likewise influences this mode. Almost all the material features of modern life actually originated in other people, most of them long dead.

Can we want what we want? Both "we" and "want" are very largely influenced by human society. The extent of the gift which each new human being receives on his journey through life is very great indeed, but the obligatory ties associated with it are equally large. Society alone makes it possible for us to want so many kinds of things. On the other hand, society largely dictates the direction of our prevailing desires.

Beyond that, society influences the individual in numerous other ways. There is, first, the phenomenon of mood transmission—an innate dependence which is equally operative in all social animals. Specific expressive movements on the part of others elicit reactions from us which are hard to control. Human beings react abnormally in the mass. The necessity for individual decision making largely disappears, as does the responsibility for what is done. We all know to what mass reactions can lead. Members of a group can be far more courageous and ruthless—or timid and irresolute. The individual becomes, in a sense, a part of a larger will which carries him along and neutralizes his normal reactions. The larger and more homogenous the group, the more the individual's movements conform to its flow. The human will is greatly influenced. A man can free himself from such manipulation of his instincts only if the "government" which dominates his parliament of instincts retains a firm hold on the reins of action.

Man also exploits this process deliberately so that others may transmit moods of pleasure and contentment to him. A large gathering of people can transmit pleasurable tension and an agreeable sense of relaxation. Festivities and entertainments are popular with people because they bring the individuals involved release from their normal selves and desires, cause them to feel wanted, and allow them to be subjected to a number of alien reactions. Music and dancing are aids to this process. Concerted rhythm helps reduce the emotions of the many to a common denominator, break down barriers, and persuade each individual to yield to the same stimulation. Laughter breeds laughter. In a crowded theater, communal reactions reinforce the normal reactions of the individual.

That which we generally call the herd instinct is only partly rooted in this phenomenon, for it contains other ingredients as well. One of them is the child's strongly developed imitative urge, which, like that of curiosity, continues to influence human actions beyond maturity. In this instance it is not the expressive movements of other people which transmit mood, but other people's actions which stimulate us to do likewise. Our intellect and imagination play a predominant part in this process. The ability to imitate is found only in the most intelligent learners and is far more evident in man than in any other. The imitative urge is therefore a form of instinctive behavior which only developed fully in man and which influences us very decisively. This instinct is the source of incentive and ambition, as well as of envy and dislike. The knowledge that other people possess abilities or artificial organs which we lack but find desirable frustrates our imitative urge and causes feelings of discontent. The desire to imitate presupposes an ability to visualize oneself with someone else's qualities and is thus linked with mental activity. We cannot aspire to possess that which we are incapable of imagining.

This instinct to imitate has proved a very important spur to human development. One man's progress kindles a desire in others for similar advancement. The same instinct has been largely responsible for the continuance of custom and usage: That which others do becomes desirable. Such influencing of values works in both directions. Something which is considered satisfactory today may lose its appeal tomorrow because another man owns or does something better. In this way, our desires are stimulated and directed in a particular direction—even against our better judgment. And in the same way, the community influences the individual and kindles desires and emotions in him which would not otherwise exist.

Closely related to this instinct is the human desire to impress, the intention being to surpass others rather than merely to emulate them. Innate forms of impressive behavior are widely found in animals. Suitable behavior impresses a prospective mate on the one hand and, on the other, among creatures which live in groups, demonstrates the individual's standing within the group. Whether the human urge to impress also depends upon hereditary fixation is still an unexplored question, but it certainly serves a basically similar purpose. Children demonstrate this behavior clearly, and it is developed even more markedly in adults. Our striving for success, esteem, and power, for social acceptance and standing, for recognition, superiority, and admiration, is seldom the product of sober deliberation but rooted in an urge which may also stem from one member of the parliament of instincts. It impairs our judgment, affects our behavior toward other people, influences the course of conversations and negotiations, causes annoyance and frustration, imparts a sense of power, and hounds a man into the recesses of his imagination. This urge endows each failure with a particularly corrosive effect; contempt and repudiation on the part of others renders it unusually bitter. To be vanquished or inferior, to be condescended to, to be mocked, ignored, or looked at askance by others—all these things provoke unpleasant tensions against which we are comparatively powerless. If people work far harder than is necessary just to maintain life and security, if they are ruled by a restless impulse to improve their lot, the underlying motive is often that of the urge to impress. The stimulus situation which releases these forces within us is invariably the behavior of other people. Here, the will of the individual displays another and particularly marked form of dependence upon society. The wise man ultimately overcomes this particular form of vanity and ceases to measure his own activities by those of others. Obviously, few people succeed in doing this.

One especially crude method of influencing the individual's will is to subject him to the authority of another. As we have already mentioned, no artificial organ is more susceptible of universal employment than man himself. Once in another's power, he can be made to do almost anything that his master does not wish to do himself. Human beings exploited this possibility from the first. The result was every conceivable kind of slavery, the subjugation of one group by another, the subordination of nations to the will of other nations. The power the head of a family exercised over his children and other members of the clan formed a natural basis for this development. The foremost individual in a tribe enjoyed a similar position of power. Monarchies and dictatorships developed huge apparatuses of power which amounted to artificial organs wielded by a single individual. There was a growth of privileged classes which set a hereditary seal on their authority by means of appropriate legislation. Similar positions of power were created by ideologies, specialized knowledge, and the possession of money. These, in turn, met every conceivable form of resistance—hence war and revolution. Today we live in a world split into two large camps: on the one hand, power systems modeled after the Communist formula for living; on the other, the countries with a democratic, free-enterprise system. What does this development signify from the biological viewpoint, and how does it affect the question of whether we can want what we want?

The power systems spawned by the Communist formula for living are very similar to organisms. The community is concerned with industry and the satisfaction of consumers' needs, and these are not the concern of the individual. The individual can be rewarded for special achievements, but the product of his labor belongs, in principle, to the community rather than to him. His legitimate claims on the community are equally circumscribed. The same conditions clearly apply to multicellular bodies. The organism as a whole pursues a livelihood and distributes the product among its functional units. It cares for them, tends them, supplies their needs, shields them from danger. In both cases, "value" attaches only to those units which perform some useful function within the framework of the work-sharing system—in other words, those which perform productive work. Units which fail to do so forfeit their right to exist and are rejected or become subject to involution. Viewed in this way, the thought-control characteristic of Communist countries is a natural and logical consequence of the system. Anything which affects the performance of a functional unit is "bad" in terms of the total system and must therefore be isolated from it where possible. Anything which serves the interests of the community is "good," however sharply it may conflict with the interests of the individual. Under this political system, personal enrichment at others' expense and exploitation of the community for personal profit are a cancerous growth which likewise begins to proliferate independently and is not in the general interests of the body. Since man has a strong inherent—and probably innate—urge to form groups and submit to a common will, the readiness to adopt this course of action not only exists but can be considerably reinforced by suitable persuasion. When fulfilled, this impulse confers intense feelings of happiness. The limitation of individual interests can arouse resentment, but education and habit—and, above all, protection from disruptive influences—can enable the human being to attain a strong and secure sense of contentment even under this political system.

What occurs here, from the biological point of view, can now be defined more precisely on the basis of our earlier considerations. The organisms which we have classified in the third subkingdom (human specialists) are embodied in a system belonging to the fourth subkingdom (productive organizations). The peculiarity of man's individual differentiation disappears again, and man dives back into the life process. The personal element disintegrates and coalesces with the superindividual totality. The manifold opportunities for human development are curtailed. The activities of the individual are limited to functions required by the community. The productive systems of the third subkingdom, in which true human development occurs, become components of superordinate power complexes.

The "collective"—the organism—determines what is worthwhile and what is worthless and dictates the prevailing direction of the general will. The multiplicity of variously oriented egos turns into functional units, or organs, in a more stable and highly integrated structure.

By contrast, the democratic free-enterprise system stimulates the development of the third subkingdom. Coercive subjugation of individuals by other individuals is still prohibited, but in other areas the individual's search for power is encouraged. The state is supposed to protect communal interests, especially from outside intervention, and is to that extent another organism. In other respects, however, and particularly internally, its function is intended to be that of a communal organ shared by all citizens. Consequently, this system favors all processes in which human individuality develops most fully. Today, however, this path also leads to the collective, to the fusion of individuals, to their coalescence in an alien will. The true circumstances are far harder to comprehend here than in the Communist state. Here, the life process has begun a new and remarkable evolutionary trend.

The start of this new and different route toward loss of freedom is the commercial form of human product exchange. One man supplies services or manufactures products for which another has some use. Thus, the seller's livelihood always rests on people who need his product, in other words, the market. He has to know and nurse his market—even create it, if need be. Special institutions designed to accomplish this include market research on the one hand and advertising on the other.

Once again, human instincts play their part. The ability to impress depends, in essence, upon some form of self-assertion—or, more precisely, upon the influencing of receptive mechanisms in fellow members of the species. In man, this leads to a development of artificial organs which is reminiscent of other creatures. Just as bright plumage or majestic manes and horns developed in form and color as aids to an imposing appearance, so man reinforced his ability to impress with the aid of handsome clothing, jewelry, and the like. The further possibility also arose of demonstrating power through the possession of more exclusive artificial organs. The designer dress, the foreign car, the architect-designed house—all these artificial organs acquire a function supplementary to their normal functions: They become, additionally, organs designed to impress. From this it follows that innumerable things can be rendered desirable to man—or, rather, forced upon him—which he does not need from the functional point of view. They accentuate the impression he makes on others and intensify his pleasurable sense of power. Further support is lent by the imitative urge, which likewise prompts man to acquire things for which he initially has little or no desire. Man thus surrounds himself with more artificial organs than he needs, and the desire to acquire them increases his willingness to work. His individuality wanes, and he becomes part of the market—in other words, one who serves another's interests.

Sales technique proved to be an essential weapon in the competitive struggle between individual members of the same calling. It was soon found that buyers could not only be located but stimulated. Vance Packard's *The Hidden Persuaders* gives a graphic account of ways in which sales are stimulated in the United States. The same development—an essential feature of our time—has swept the rest of the democratic free-enterprise world. The primary objective is to penetrate the human subconscious so as to impel innate or acquired behavior mechanisms in the desired direction. The secondary objective is to depreciate a man's property as quickly as possible, use every available means to destroy his pleasure in what he has already acquired, and enhance the desirability of what he does not already possess. The first line of attack stimulates man's instincts —his animal heritage—and harnesses them for the benefit of commercial interests. The second method deprives an owner of the ability to check and evaluate his artificial organs and reduces him to a permanent condition of wanting more. Our love of novelty is proving to be a menace in this respect, and our aesthetic sense—the basis of all culture—is likewise being exploited in order to force our desires along channels which serve a commercial interest of some kind.

The democratic free-enterprise system, as it is currently developing, threatens to lead ultimately to a situation where each strives to kindle desires in others and is, conversely, infected with similar desires by others. It is only logical that children, being particularly impressionable, should be influenced from an early age so as to become part of the market later on, and this absorption of influence continues throughout life. Newspapers, films, and television are direct or indirect aids to this process. Everything which attains value—works of art, ideas, or achievements—is linked in some way with the interests of a would-be seller. Little escapes this commercializing tendency today—indeed, most people have become totally unaware of the process. The absorption of influence has gone so far that "merit" and "sales value" coincide almost completely. Every conceivable form of demand is explored and stimulated, and the products or services suggested by this research are offered for sale. Progress receives a powerful fillip in this way—not in its true guise, however, but in its capacity as a sales product. The result is endless activity and an incessant stimulation of new demand. Because the individual is constantly offered aids to happiness, he has little if any time to reflect whether such aids bring him genuine and lasting contentment. Ultimately this trend will create, in biological terms, a spongelike social structure whose components are inextricably entangled, each at one and the same time operating on the others and being influenced by them—a system which feeds upon, erodes, and paralyzes itself, a system in which the individual is just as surely lost as in the Communist one.

The Western world is thus following a quite different road from the Communist world. It evolves different structures yet ultimately achieves a similar result. Here, too, man's peculiarity is extinguished. Manipulated by an immensely powerful society, he has no time to reflect on himself. He is absorbed, not by the interests of the state, but by a far more complex process which also guides, molds, and extinguishes his individuality.

Is another course open?

If so, it might consist in man's regaining control over his artificial organs—in his realizing that these structures should serve *him,* not their manufacturer.

Man, as Aristotle said long ago, is a social being who attains self-development only through society. We must develop a greater awareness of the immense gift with which each of us is sent on his way through life. This might not inspire true charity, but it would encourage a stronger sense of global solidarity. On the other hand, it is just as important to achieve a greater awareness of the sinister power of the anonymous plurality which has engendered us. Its tendency to absorb us in one way or another is second only to the possibility of self-annihilation as a threat to our essential humanity.

17

Man and Imagination

O F man's many peculiarities, perhaps the most significant is his power of imagination. It is the true key to his essential nature and success. As far as we have been able to establish by experiments, man is the only animal capable of combining memories and experiences to whatever extent he desires. He can, mentally, bring any specific thing in the world into conjunction with any other. He can, so to speak, dream while he is awake and steer his dreams in any desired direction. He can devise courses of action for himself—lay plans— and check his memory to determine if they are practicable on the basis of past experience. He can combine experience or logic with his imagination and test the resultant thoughts within his mind for practicality. Man's brain provides him with a sort of screen upon which he can project and construct his ideas. There, future can be blended with past, components removed and replaced with others, the flow of ideas accelerated, slowed, or repeated at will.

The biological significance of this special faculty of our central nervous system is great. For one thing, it represents a vast saving of energy. We do not have to perform an action in order to discover whether or not it is of practical value. We can explore it within our mind. We can review the numerous courses of action open to us with most decisions and select the one with the greatest prospect of success—and this without exercising a single muscle. We can devise plans whose ultimate goal lies years in the future and thousands of miles distant. We can examine each individual link in such a chain of action by itself—investigate, test, mold, or discard it. We can make discoveries—originate new ideas—within ourselves by repeatedly juggling with alternatives. In this way, we can discover relationships which lead us to the formation of useful structures, a process which we call invention. In short, we can perform, achieve, discover, and deduce a thousand (if not a million) times as much as the life-span accorded us would otherwise enable us to do.

Is this faculty also developed in animals? Virtually no scientific data are available on the subject, but what is especially lacking is a precise definition of the term "imagination." Gehlen, one of the few to have taken a close interest in this problem, espoused the view that every memory is a feat of imagination in that it summons up sensory impressions which are no longer present. Since feats of memory have been demonstrated in most of the higher animals, the implication is that this basic form of "imagination" is present in them, too. Gehlen went on to point out that a wide variety of ideas can superimpose themselves by association upon objects which are familiar to us. The sight of a refrigerator can, even before we open it, link us with the idea of the coolness prevailing inside and of the interior arrangement, with our knowledge of the door's mobility, and so on. As Gehlen very graphically put it, the objects familiar to us are surrounded by a whole "court" of expectations, alternatives, memories, and allusions. We "see" more in them than optical perception actually conveys, and this, too, Gehlen regarded as a product of the imaginative faculty. Because similar associations exist in animals, he considered that this act of imagination was present in them, too. The young human being clearly displays an ability to project a wide variety of meanings into its toys. To a girl, a building brick may become a house or a stove; a boy may see it as a car or a fortress. This is expressive of a still higher imaginative faculty, yet similar processes can be observed in learners at play. Although we cannot tell if a cat has a mental image in our sense when it plays "mice" with a cork, there is a definite analogy. Aristotle said of ideas that the power of thought constructed them on the basis of inwardly perceived images, but an ability to construct averbal ideas has been demonstrated in animals, too. Although all these phenomena are characterized by a conjunction between ideas and something which is actually perceived, what we experience in our dreams is a world of imagination which is not at all connected with direct perception. Observations suggest that animals—dogs, for instance—also undergo dreamlike experiences, and cerebral stimulation has produced phenomena suggestive of hallucination.

It is highly debatable whether all these phenomena should be included under the heading of imagination. They are, however, a clear indication that man's imaginative faculty, far from being totally new, represents an intensification of a function performed by the central nervous system in animals as well.

We might do better to restrict the scope of the term and limit it to that special faculty which is obviously peculiar to man alone: the ability to combine various ingredients of consciousness at will in the mind. A sharp dividing line separates this from the performance of the highest animal learners. As we have already mentioned, experiments with chimpanzees have shown that they are capable of solving a problem when the elements of that problem (banana, boxes, stick) are more or less simultaneously within their field of view. Superimposed on each of these objects is a certain number of experiences; by weighing them against one another, the ape's brain eventually arrives at the correct correlation. A causal nexus is discovered. Should the elements of the problem be spatially or temporally farther apart, no solution will be forthcoming. The human brain has evidently acquired a new and improved functional unit which permits a far wider if not unlimited correlation of experiential values. Our special faculty, which we call intelligence, may thus be largely derived from that other faculty which we call imagination.

Our innate instincts supply our imagination with an important source of motive power. No action ensues if one member of our parliament of instincts "speaks," but optative images flash across the screen of our imagination. If we feel hungry, they are images of food; if we are sexually aroused, sexual images; if we are aggressively inclined, images against which we can mentally direct our aggression. Moreover, imagination promptly and spontaneously devises more or less concrete plans for the satisfaction of the instincts in question. The central government—our real ego—expresses its views on the matter, rejects or approves, switches off the optative picture or leaves it running, imposes other ideas, or harnesses its own will to the attainment of the instinctive goal. Dialogues between reason and instinct are familiar to all of us from experience and have often been portrayed in literature. The battle here is for possession of our internal projection screen. The images that appear on it excite us and react upon our instincts. If we give free rein to sexual optative images, the result will be an accentuation of our sexual proclivity. If we give free rein to fear images, our fear is intensified. A significant reciprocal action results. Our instincts kindle our imagination, and our imagination reacts upon our instincts. Exactly the same applies to acquired instincts, or habits. If they prompt us to act in a certain way (e.g., drink alcohol), this is associated with corresponding optative images. If we abandon ourselves to these, they reinforce our urge. However, we can also play off one instinct against another. If hunger announces itself and we concentrate our imagination upon sexual or aggressive images, hunger may lapse into oblivion for a while. The central government, our true ego, is thus capable of a measure of control. We can, within certain limits, forbid ourselves to imagine something and thereby—again, within certain limits—inhibit the emotions associated with it. If an instinct or acquired urge becomes too strong, however, its images will flash repeatedly across our inner screen in defiance of our wishes. As often as we switch them off, they reappear. If our fear mounts, we are powerless against images that terrify us. If our anger mounts, we are tormented by ever more persistent images productive of anger. The same applies to hunger, insomnia, the urge to impress, habits—to the whole range of innate or acquired urges. So that while we can influence and manipulate instincts by means of our imagination, we can do so only to a certain degree.

It was in conjunction with our imagination, too, that the human urge to play and explore attained such preeminent importance. This impulse not only causes us to explore our environment and try out new movements; above all, it prompts us to indulge in the mental game of correlating ingredients of consciousness and exploring one avenue of the imagination after another. Man conquered the world less by his actions than by the interplay of his thoughts and ideas. This game—the game of the visionary and dreamer—is extraordinarily cheap in terms of energy. It costs us not a thousandth part of the effort needed to put the appropriate action into effect. Our mental games help us to prepare ourselves for the most diverse forms of behavior—in other words, to construct imaginative coordinations. To the best of my knowledge, nobody has yet drawn attention to the significant parallels between these structures, which we call plans, and our innate and acquired behavioral formulas. Each hereditary coordination is, as we have seen, linked with a corresponding appetency. Exactly the same is true of behavior patterns instilled by habit, or acquired coordinations. An inability to perform them not only arouses feelings of displeasure and restlessness but inspires us with an active desire to put them into effect just the same. Very much the same applies to the behavior patterns which we construct in our imagination. Once formed, a plan assumes a sort of independent existence. It declares its presence and demands to be put into effect. Success engenders a sense of satisfaction, failure an unpleasant sense of disappointment. Our illusions and ideals are no different in that respect. They are behavioral ideas which we project into the world and which prompt us to go in quest of them; failure to attain them leaves us troubled and disappointed. This relationship may well be of greater importance than first appearances would suggest because it demonstrates a functional affinity between three circuit patterns which come into being in quite different ways. Whether behavior control was built up by a hereditary formula, whether it was created by the process of learning and practice, or whether it originated through the pure exercise of our imagination, the phenomenon of spontaneous excitation occurs in every case, and appetencies declare themselves whose fulfillment or nonfulfillment gives rise to a corresponding sense of pleasure or displeasure.

Another link between imagination and instinct is found in our ability to work off unfulfilled instincts in our imagination. This applies particularly to our aggressive drive and our urge to impress. Whether we are spontaneously disposed to be aggressive or have been aggravated, whether we have only been frustrated in our urge to impress or have been actually humiliated, we can—in our imagination—wallow in revenge, annihilate our enemies, assume a commanding pose. It is these instinctive desires which are so often hard to satisfy within society. Those without power cannot pay their oppressors back in kind; the ugly or incompetent cannot hope to impress their fellowmen. Here, man's imagination becomes a substitute for that which reality forbids. It is possible, within limits, to divert pent-up excitation along this channel. Imagination enables the serf to be king, the sexually frustrated to play Casanova, the timid to display courage, the rabid to wreak universal destruction. Here lies the key to the special significance of literature. It not only imparts information but enables man to satisfy his instincts through the medium of imagination.

How to write well—the author's prime concern—is in direct line of descent from the prime concern of the storyteller, which was how to narrate well. Successful examples of narrative technique from every age convey what really matters in this art form from the scientific point of view. The aim, obviously, is to activate the various instinctive emotions of the listener—or reader—in such a way as to produce an agreeable alternation of tension and relief. The narrator conducts people—in their imagination—through a world of experience. Speech or writing must be tailored so that the transmission of the narrative content from one brain to another takes place as smoothly and uninterruptedly as possible. The plot must not unfold faster than we can follow it, nor must its pace be so slow that boredom sets in. It must take account of the multiplicity of our instinctive desires; hence, it must not be directed exclusively at only one specific instinct. It must toy with instincts, activate them in turn and set them off against one another. It must arouse tension born of fear, and then—at the proper moment—release it. It must provoke outrage and then allay it. We must feel love, see it threatened, and then watch the storm clouds roll away. The heroes in whose fate we become ensnared by imagination must experience what we wish and fear for ourselves. However the story ends, whether happily or tragically, it must hold our attention. In it, we see ourselves; in it, our emotions are manipuated, allowed to build up excitement and, ultimately, vent it. This is not to say that great writers practice such a form of manipulation consciously and calculatingly; all that is certain is that they practice it. In ethological terms, the narrator who wishes to activate our imagination successfully must offer us "supernormal series of stimuli."

We may infer how our imagination and instincts work from the way in which it is easier to stimulate our imagination. The narrator plays on them as if they were an instrument, and his method tells us a great deal about the constitution of these hidden structures, reveals how they react, how they flag, what stimulates them, and how various pleasurable sensations are brought about. In all these matters, scientific exploration of ourselves can derive clues from the rich experiences of art.

In the theater and the cinema, narrative is reinforced by direct sensory impressions. Here, the action is presented with an intensified realism which restricts the personal imagination in some ways but stimulates it in others. The action is compressed into a specific time span—whence there emerges another set of rules governing construction. These are the concern of dramaturgy, another field which has yet to be considered from the biological aspect. Additional factors are involved, notably the actor's ability to transmit mood. By expressions, gestures, and words, he conveys immediate reactions—a process which actually amounts to the offering of supernormal dummies. The actor's art consists in manipulating innate and acquired reactions as efficiently as possible. Because a play affects us partly through direct perception and not just through the imagination, the factors involved are more complex and the number of possibilities even greater.

Painting and sculpture—viewed, once again, from the scientific point of view—follow quite a different route. They appeal directly to our innate and acquired recognition mechanisms. Isolated impressions and the reactions they elicit from us are the factor involved here. One particular area of our nervous functions is plumbed to its depths. Perhaps today's most consistent explorer of this domain is Picasso. By incorporating a succession of new elements in his representational technique, weighing and playing them off against one another, he has explored the abysses of our subconscious. In this art form, a special element occupies the foreground: acquired modes of recognition and evaluation, or, in other words, our taste. This plays a role in literature, the theater, and the cinema, too, but only a subordinate one because the center of the stage is occupied by human life and passions. Outward form may also adapt itself to contemporary taste, but the phenomena which excite us are ultimately the same. It is different with painting and sculpture, where acquired taste may be the decisive factor. To the painter or sculptor the fundamental criterion of his work is his own reaction to it. Nevertheless, his personal taste may be so remote from that of others that his work elicits false reactions from them or none at all. It can happen, therefore, that an artist ultimately does no more than satisfy the reactions of his own central nervous system, or that a limited circle develops a sensitivity geared to special criteria which mean nothing to the rest of their contemporaries. In this case, too, the artist provides supernormal stimulus situations for the release of ideas and sensations, but their effect depends predominantly on acquired forms of recognition and is thus confined to people whose brains have developed suitable receptive structures.

This also applies to music, probably the art which acts most directly upon our emotions. Certain basic elements in the juxtaposition of sounds may arouse similar emotions in all people (solemn, tragic, cheerful), but reactions once again depend largely upon acquired recognition mechanisms. The Westerner, for example, derives little or no aesthetic pleasure from classical Japanese music. Upbringing and, possibly, imprinting play an important part in this. The various plastic and graphic arts appeal to the purely spatial components of our aesthetic judgment; music appeals to the purely temporal. *Immediate* effects are focal to both forms of art, but both forms can operate indirectly through our imagination. We can also allow all kinds of works of art to work on us through imagination, just as the artist does when creating them. Our imaginative projection

screen is aural as well as visual and embraces all forms of sen
sory perception.

We have hitherto confined our examination to one aspect o
art, namely, its effect on other people and the problem of wha
makes it effective. The essence of art—its true ability—lies else
where. Comparisons are often and with justification drawn be
tween the artist and the scientist on the grounds that each seek
knowledge and truth in his own way. The scientist looks fo
objective and measurable relationships. The artist pursues
subjective quest for knowledge and truth. He strives to crystal
lize what is peculiar to his own experience of life and condens
plurality into a comprehensible structure, whether narrative
pictorial, or musical. There is, however, a close relationship be
tween the human forming of ideas and the special activity o
the artist. The forming of ideas, on which all man's thinking i
based, depends upon the perception of common and typica
features in similar phenomena—undoubtedly a feat of imagina
tion because the common element is always something imag
ined and situated ultimately in ourselves. We associate ou
conception of what is common with a verbal symbol—for in
stance, we refer to everything that grows a trunk, branches
and leaves as a tree. As Gehlen emphasized, this inner connec
tion between a conceptual structure and a certain series o
sounds (spoken and heard) is a peculiar feat of the imagination
and one which animals achieve only in exceptional cases. The
artist does something basically similar, except on a higher plane
He endeavors to crystallize the totality of an experience in sym
bolic terms; hence, his work of art is as much a symbol of this
greater totality as a word is that of a (usually simpler) con
cept. Whether in the form of a narrative, spatial image, or
temporal sound pattern, the artist's symbol is always subjective,
being the product of his abstractive act of condensing plurality
into an ordered unity. In this capacity—the essence of art—a
"better" and a "worse" can be distinguished. The truly great
artist, who can grasp the special features of his subject, must
possess a second, synthetic, capacity for transmitting this im
pression to the brains of others and conveying his newly formed
concept to them as well. It may one day be demonstrated that
man has an innate urge to form concepts. Indeed, considering

the exceptional importance which this process has for us, it would not be surprising. If this were true, however, one might advance the theory that an artist is characterized by a particularly strong set of impulses in this direction. His hypertrophic striving to form concepts would thus manifest itself in an urge to form concepts of a higher order, concepts which he condenses into symbols and strives to introduce into the consciousness of others.

The genesis of primitive religions may also be traced to similar processes. As soon as man acquired the ability to combine elements of experience in his head, as soon as he was able, mentally, to survey causes and effects which did not lie within his immediate range of perception, as soon as he summarized the physical world in terms of concepts and labeled them with word symbols, he left the uncomplicated paradise, "ate of the Tree of Knowledge," and encountered a variety of frightening and worrying problems which taxed his imagination. Phenomena such as thunder and lightning demanded explanation. The ideas of supernatural forces, spirits, and gods may be necessary consequences of the burgeoning of causal thought, a process whereby imagination converts the inexplicable into a comprehensible something in just the same way as it extracts the common elements from perceived phenomena. Once formed, however, such ideas constituted an ideal dreamworld to which everything could be related. Anything that troubled man or was incomprehensible to him could be ascribed to the workings of these self-created products of his imagination. And by being handed down by word of mouth from one generation to the next, they acquired an almost unshakable reality.

Thus, invisible properties superimposed themselves upon numerous objects or occurrences, rendering them sacred, taboo, or execrable. The appeasement and influencing of gods by sacrifice and ceremonial was a natural consequence of the belief in their existence. These ideas presented leaders of human communities with a welcome opportunity to link the rules of community life with some higher authority. Existing or projected systems of government could thus be given a stronger and more stable foundation in this way. Morality and law were more easily anchored to figments of the imagination than to any more real authority, because fear of the unknown always exceeded fear of the familiar. Men of artistic bent were necessarily encouraged to develop these ideas still further. The impulse to submit found an optimal stimulus situation in which to fulfill itself through self-abasement. Man thus created—like a work of art of a very special kind—a world of the imagination which reacted upon, guided, and fulfilled him. It became the invisible backbone of individual civilizations, a criterion of action, a bond which strengthened the community—in short, an institution of high selective value. Viewing things in this light, we can understand how such ideas first originated in every center of human development. This is not to say that every religion represents an imaginary structure of this kind. From the scientific aspect, not a single religious idea is capable of refutation. This applies even to the most primitive religions, even those that have become extinct. All that we are concerned to show here is how the phenomenon of our imagination, in conjunction with our capacity for causal thought, positively demanded the forming of supersensual ideas. This furnishes a plausible explanation of how these ideas took shape in such large numbers and with such regularity, and why—once in existence— they were so stubbornly retained.

And with that we come to the opposite side of the coin. Imagination is not only a human asset, not only the basis of discovery and progress, not only a means of satisfying our unfulfilled urges and providing ourselves with "mental" sensations of pleasure, but something which debilitates and threatens mankind. It is, in a sense, our most vulnerable spot. When Kant said that imagination was our good or evil genius, he meant that it could—given a particular set of values—lead us into good or evil ways. What interests us here, however, is another of imagination's negative effects—and this brings us back to the question of whether we are at all capable of wanting what we want.

Because our imagination can be so easily manipulated by ourselves and others, it becomes the natural means whereby other people's influence gains access to us. Speech and writing especially help to project ideas on our internal screen which activate our innate or acquired emotions willy-nilly. The ego that rules us can resist these ideas, but when they are presented in a way which disguises their dangers, we may be involuntarily swayed by them. The invariable procedure is that emotions and reactions are aroused in us by the kindling of our imagination. Advertising and propaganda are especially purposeful examples of this. Science itself is enlisted in order to dislodge our ego from its prepared defenses and manipulate our reactions so as to inject us with another's will. This is the subtlest and most sinister form of enslavement. As a means of transforming us—without our knowledge—into artificial organs controlled by an outside agency, it is the most dangerous of all.

The greatest threat to which man's imagination indirectly exposes him lies in demagogy and the deliberate fanning of national sentiment. This process precedes the outbreak of every war and may one day result in our self-annihilation.

Once again, we are dealing with an activation of instincts which link us closely with our animal past. The first and most important of these is the social aggression which welds gregarious creatures into a fighting unit. This expresses itself in the social defensive reaction, a phenomenon exhaustively studied in rhesus monkeys, baboons, and howling monkeys. It is stimulated in these creatures by the sight of a strange group of monkeys of the same species and leads to a battle for the territory in question. As Lorenz has suggested, the sense of national exaltation so sacred to human beings, far from being human or sacred, derives from the analogous instinct which—by spontaneous production of excitation—leads to self-forming appetitive behavior. The concomitant physiological symptoms which occur in man are very similar to those in apes, which will likewise sacrifice their lives for the community. Apes, too, goad one another by the emission of rhythmical sounds comparable in effect to martial music, and there are various other parallels as well. We shall probably find it harder to reassess this precious and much-praised reaction than any other, because it springs from an instinct which has us at its mercy. We derive pleasure from yielding to it, and we associate it with our highest and most ancient ideals. It declares itself in every group, whether it be a circle of young people, a club, a community of ideas, or a nation. In man, the social defensive reaction can—like all instinctive behavior—be activated through the imagination. Accounts of the enemy's evil may be exaggerated to any desired degree because our capacity for rational thought is not equal to the idea of atrocities and maltreatment. As an additional aid, our natural fears may be played upon. We are told that we must fight because we cannot do otherwise; if not, our goods and chattels will be seized, our wives raped, our children maltreated, our lives forfeited. In other words, we must destroy in order to avoid destruction. Two more instincts are also enlisted as aids: greed and the sexual urge. The enemy's property and womenfolk are open to conquest. If the rational ego remains unaffected in such circumstances, it is a positive miracle. Afterward, the community demands to know how it all came about. The demagogue is execrated but not his principal tool: the imagination of his dupes.

Is there a way out, or will mankind continue to tread the same path?

If man desires freedom, some freedoms will have to be curtailed. The dangers that confront us are simply becoming too great, and no amount of education and enlightenment will substantially change this fact. Sporting contests, theatrical performances, and similar diversions provide man with certain opportunities to work off his aggressive tendencies, but this is not enough. We also need protection from certain forms of influence.

Imagination is at once our great strength and our great weakness. It resembles the fire which Prometheus stole from the gods, and for which he was chained to the rocks. It is, perhaps, the most singular of our possessions—the most human element in humanity. As a faculty, however, it also resembles the leaf which dropped on to Siegfried's shoulder and rendered him vulnerable in that one spot. Imagination makes man exceptionally vulnerable. He will always remain so.

18

The Quest for Happiness

M AN has made his first landing on the moon. It remains
to be seen whether his immense investment of energy
in this form of exploratory behavior will bear fruit,
but one result can already be foreseen today. Access to the moon
presents scientists with a unique opportunity. If they succeed
in constructing a huge telescope there, it will be possible—since
the moon has no atmosphere to interfere with the passage of
light—to look a little farther into the limitless universe. We
shall then be able to observe cosmic phenomena millions of
light-years away and gain an even clearer recognition of just
how tiny a spatial and temporal phenomenon we ourselves are.

Let us assume that an astronomer stationed on the moon has
stolen a few hours from his research program to look at the
earth purely for his own pleasure. Let us further assume that
his telescope is powerful enough to enable him to observe the
activities of individual human beings. What does he see?

He sees us for what we really are—creatures that dwell all
over a sphere. In other words, he sees something which we find
hard to imagine (although we *know* it perfectly well) because
our top-and-bottom orientation has the *a priori* fixity of a Kant-
ian category. He sees how the people situated on the upper
side of this globe—in other words, the side which happens to
accord with his own position—walk upright. Aiming his telescope at the side of the globe, he sees people strolling about
and engaging in other activities at 90 degrees from the per-

pendicular. Finally, turning to the bottom of the globe, he sees airplanes taking off downward and couples courting on secluded benches, oblivious of time and place and unaware that they are—to him—upside down. In short, he sees us in our true perspective, and the spectacle may possibly serve to illustrate a human peculiarity which we take even more for granted than all the rest: our quest for happiness.

As soon as our planet—a mere grain of sand in cosmic terms —produced the requisite conditions, its surface witnessed a process which expressed itself in the formation of increasingly complicated and efficient structures. So far as we can tell today, this process had no real goal or objective save that of self-enlargement. In this respect, life resembles a fire which seeks nourishment and employs it to promote its own growth. Fire, too, requires energy and converts it into part of its process. This also applies to the life process, which also seeks utilizable energy which likewise becomes a component and, in turn, the real activator of the process. The great difference is that the life process manifests itself in the formation of ordered structures which facilitate the active procurement of energy and are, in this sense, useful. These structures not only grow but, within the natural limits imposed upon them by, say, terrestrial gravity or their own organization's restricted ability to expand, multiply as well. If the life process had not developed both these faculties, it would swiftly have ground to a halt. It did, in fact, develop them and so perpetuated itself. Scientifically, Nietzsche's contention that the sole purpose behind this process is a will to power can scarcely be refuted. On the other hand, a similar will may be attributed to fire, though on a far less complicated scale.

Each of us—each human being—is a similar productive system, a similar order attained by the life process, and the most complex and powerful of all. We are the only such systems to be able—in our imagination—to assess ourselves, review our own lives, and deliberately shape them. In us, the life process reached a point at which blind will was joined by reflection—in other words, the ability to affect the direction of that will. In what direction is man now steering it? Our activities have become vastly complicated, but what is their ultimate objective?

All systems engendered by the life process share the fundamental ability to assess what is conducive or not conducive to that process. This discriminative faculty is controlled in accordance with what biologists call the pleasure-pain principle. Living creatures react positively to many perceptions, are attracted by them, as it were, and gravitate toward them. These stimuli cause them pleasure; others, which repel them and provoke withdrawal or aversion, cause them pain. We cannot tell if these pleasing and painful sensations are comparable with the human sort because we cannot communicate with plants and other animals. Certain schools of psychology are therefore justified in pointing out that we ought not to make inferences about animals' sensations from our own. On the other hand, it can scarcely be doubted that our sensations depend upon the pleasure-pain discrimination which characterizes the entire life process—indeed, is its central driving force.

The salient point—and here we come to another crucial human peculiarity—is that we are not only aware of pleasurable sensations but can recognize the causality of their origin. Because we realize what such sensations do for us, it is only natural that we should use our intelligence to promote pleasurable conditions and prevent disagreeable conditions to the best of our ability. Further than that, we change matters or bring about artificially contrived situations so as to enhance our state of pleasure. The most powerful sources of pleasure are our innate instincts. These function in such a way that the attainment of a given instinctive goal engenders pleasurable sensations, whereas nonattainment produces disagreeable ones. This is why innate behavior patterns have always been a focal human interest. It is clear that our ancestors early succeeded in making these positive sensations—originally no more than a necessary cog in the total mechanism of species preservation—a definite objective. In other words, the means became an end in itself.

This development has gone far indeed, one example being our feeding habits. We have long ceased to eat merely to introduce a requisite quantity of nourishment into our bodies; instead, by suitable preparation and seasoning, we have increased the power of food to bestow pleasure on us. For many people, the problem has ceased to be how to eat enough to stay healthy;

but rather how to eat as well and as abundantly as possible without impairing their health. Such an example alone suffices to show how novel this development is from the evolutionary standpoint. Hitherto directed outward and aimed at assimilating alien substances, expanding and propagating itself, the life process is now, as it were, turning against itself and aiming at the activation of processes inherent in itself. To put it crudely, man is becoming an exploiter of his own pleasure-bestowing mechanisms—a very singular parasite which lives on its own nerve structure. He has become a specialist in enjoyment and, consequently, a civilized being.

Linguistic usage has endowed the words "exploit," "parasite," and—above all—"hedonistic" with a negative connation which has no place in this discussion. From the cosmic, sober, and unprejudiced viewpoint for which we are striving here, each living creature is an exploiter and a parasite. Plants exploit the source of energy represented by the sun's rays and are thus sunlight parasites. All creatures use the bodies of certain other organisms, whether animal or vegetable, as a source of energy; the fact that they exploit these other bodies makes them a kind of parasite. We normally restrict the definition of parasite to those animals (and plants) which attach themselves to others and feed on them continuously. In our subjective human view, this method of obtaining nourishment is repellent—probably an innate reaction which we reserve for our own parasites and transfer to all analogous natural processes unconnected with us. From the biological point of view—that of the life process—this form of existence is no worse than any other. Indeed, ethical judgments such as good and bad have no foundation here. The only valid criterion is "viable" or "nonviable." We are exploiters and parasites of cattle, fruit, grain, and so forth. What is so novel and unusual about man is not, therefore, that he is an exploiter and parasite, since these terms are applicable to all living creatures. Our true peculiarity is that although the acquisition of energy (and matter) remains important and necessary, it is no longer our central goal or real objective but has become a means of obtaining something else. This something else, which has thus become our true aim in life, consists of pleasurable sensations—in other words, concomitant features of our life process. To obtain these, man engages in far greater exertions than are necessary to the maintenance of life. Naturally, there is nothing bad about this form of exploitation, or autoparasitism, provided it does nothing to impair viability. However, man has gained such superiority over all other creatures that he can afford the luxury of cultivating his own pleasurable sensations. By so doing he is giving the life process a new and singular twist—one which is vaguely discernible in certain other creatures (notably domestic animals) but which in our case, by reason of our conscious intelligence, has become the central feature of our development.

The word "pleasure" is equally subject to misunderstanding because many manifestations of pleasure have acquired an unfavorable tang. We regard intense interest in food or sex as "animal" and morally objectionable, whereas heightened sensations of pleasure derived from the brood-tending urge or our social instincts—that is, intense pleasure in the welfare of children or an act of friendliness toward another—impress us as good and justified. This in part depends upon religious criteria, but Lorenz has suggested that the distinction probably derives from an innate reaction. As soon as "primitive" instincts which are old in terms of evolutionary history attain a functional pitch exceeding the norm, we regard them as bad; in those that are in process of regression, we regard an analogous excess as praiseworthy. This is, as it were, a correction applied to the deviation from the natural selective principle created by domestication. To the biologist, the term "pleasure" has no such favorable or unfavorable connotation but embraces all processes of excitation insofar as these have a positive tendency—in other words, cause an organism to respond to or persevere in a stimulus situation. However, because the term has no such neutral connotation in daily use, it does not lend itself to further employment here and should be replaced by another which, though current among philosophers and poets, is seldom used by scientists. This is the concept of being happy or, simply, happiness. It has the great merit of being almost entirely neutral: happiness may be associated equally with an orgasm or sensations derived from the appreciation of art; a soft bed can make us as happy as a mark of public recognition, as the birth of a child, as the ruthless crushing of an opponent. Although a quite temporary condition may be called happiness (a moment's happiness), we generally describe people as happy if agreeable sensations predominate in them for considerable periods, if their conduct and attitude to life is such that they persevere more or less continuously in a state of being happy—a condition which may embrace a large number of individual sensations.

Man modified drinking, as well as eating, in order to increase its pleasure-bestowing properties—in other words, he learned to employ it as a means of intensifying his state of happiness. We even exploit the respiratory function when we smoke tobacco. The flight urge, which expresses itself in fear, is strongly developed in us. This instinct originally responded to dangerous animals, strangers, unfamiliar surroundings and natural phenomena. Thanks to our capacity for causal thought, it extended to a far larger number of circumstances which we find menacing in some way and which therefore arouse anxiety. The same instinct gave rise to our urge for security, which we satisfy when concealing ourselves for purposes of sleep or sexual intercourse. It also gave rise to an immense number of contrivances which endow man with a pleasurable sense of security: burglar-proof houses, fences, weapons, defensive alliances, insurance policies, much legislation, territorial defense installations, the police, the courts, prisons, and many other things. A considerable percentage of the taxes paid by a citizen represents the price of security. As we have already emphasized, man cannot work off his equally strong aggressive urge in a well-ordered society without undesirable consequences. Instead, he obtains the sensations of happiness it can bestow by indulging in socially acceptable rather than violent conflict, by intrigue and artifice, by attending boxing matches and races (at which he identifies himself with the contestants), by sporting activities, theaters, films, and much else besides. Anyone who cannot fight his own battles (or is inhibited by excessive feelings of fear) has a chance of attaining this source of pleasure through the medium of his imagination. We derive happiness from our brood-tending urge by making our families happy. The social instincts—left far behind by the scale of modern mass society—bestow pleasure on us when we indulge in social get-togethers and the festivals which men have devised the world over; we derive sensations of happiness from national enthusiasm and fighting spirit (sentiments which have become exceedingly dangerous); we derive happiness from membership in a group, from championing an idea, from espousing a doctrine. Other products of this instinctive behavior—additionally influenced by the sexual urge—are the intense human striving for status and the pleasurable sense of power associated with impressing other people, with the attainment of superior positions, titles, decorations, and marks of distinction. The impulse toward order—if such a thing is indeed a hereditary fixation—bestows sensations of happiness on us when we are successful in the coordination of processes, men at work and women in the home. The exploratory urge brings joy through the medium of variety, games, gambling—even danger. Flocks of modern tourists exploit this happiness-bestowing reaction in the same way as the masses congregated in cinemas and before television screens. The sexual urge brings singularly intense feelings of happiness ranging from the purely physical to the mental and spiritual, and the far-reaching effects of this particular quest for happiness are universally familiar. Closely linked with it is our innate faculty for aesthetic appreciation. This has led to culture in the true sense, in that we do, where possible, mold our manifold artificial organs in such a way that they not only serve us within the context of their function (in addition to being a means of impressing others) but also delight us by their beauty, in other words, bestow feelings of aesthetic satisfaction upon us. The motor instinct, the linguistic instinct, and other innate proclivities likewise prompt us to actions whose performance brings us happiness.

It is characteristic of human instinctive behavior that our instincts are no longer rigidly allied with fixed hereditary coordinations and that we no longer respond selectively to clearly defined key stimuli. Rigid motor sequences broke down in the case of learners, as we have already discussed, and our own mechanisms of innate recognition have also lost their selectivity because of human self-domestication. In practice, this means that although our instincts have survived—and in many cases gained in strength—they seldom lead to strictly prescribed motor sequences and respond to a wide variety of environmental situations. This accounts for the obscurity of our instincts—the "dark urge," as Goethe called it. If one of them responds to suitable stimuli—or declares its presence by spontaneously producing excitation—we become restive without immediately recognizing the direction of the urge. Only when a "switch-off" situation has been found in which the urge finds an outlet and brings us sensations of happiness do we recognize the instinctive goal that has been attained, register it, and later go in search of it again. Experience thus renders our instinctive behavior more selective: We gradually learn what we want. Since instincts vary greatly in strength from individual to individual, different instincts may predominate in different people. In addition, there are the acquired norms of action and reaction, which, when sufficiently well established, also turn into urges whose timely fulfillment arouses feelings of happiness. Finally, there are the motor sequences formed in the imagination—plans and illusions—which also behave like instincts and bring feelings of happiness when put into effect. The human body may be compared to a cart drawn by a wide assortment of horses, all pulling in different directions. The driver, the self-aware ego, is dormant when the cart embarks on its journey through the world. At first it is the existing or innate horses which pull the cart, guided by parents and society. Gradually, the driver asserts his authority, receiving countless pieces of advice en route and striving to get a firm grip on the reins. He acquires more horses, and these must be curbed, too. The journey—one of business and pleasure combined—leads through a forbidding jungle of regulations peculiar to the district. Obstacles and difficulties abound, each horse requires feeding and tries to take the bit between its teeth. Often, too, the members of the team make the driver's task still more difficult by pulling against one another.

Intellectuals and poets of every age have debated the best way of driving the cart smoothly and attaining as permanent a state of happiness as possible. Their legacies of opinion and advice are often diametrically opposed. Many (Nietzsche, for instance) saw happiness in self-aggrandizement and the surmounting of obstacles; others (like Chuang-tze) recommended total abstention from power and frenzied exertion. The Cyrenaic school of philosophy founded by Aristippus declared that everything which bestowed pleasure was conducive to happiness and therefore good; another school, the Stoics, declared that pleasure was a fetter, a limitation upon freedom, that it made people unhappy and was therefore bad. According to Horace, whose views are more popular than most, property brings happiness. Diogenes—and many another since his day—showed that happiness and contentment can also be founded on lack of property. According to the Jewish, Christian, and Moslem faiths, happiness reposes in another existence. Goethe declared that happiness is to be found everywhere in the world, though he did say at another point that it is always present where one does not happen to be. Hölderlin tells us that happiness is harder to endure than unhappiness. Cicero held that happiness subsists in desire rather than fulfillment. Seneca's view was that happiness contains the seeds of its own downfall. Lao-tse advised people to renounce happiness in order to gain it—and so on.

One characteristic of happiness which has taxed the minds of many thinkers is its mysterious impermanence. It dances along like a will-o'-the-wisp, tempting human beings to grasp it and vanishing into thin air when they try. Mysterious though it appears, this process has its almost commonplace explanation in the phenomenon of the varying stimulus threshold. A thirsty man trudges through the desert, and the stronger his craving for water becomes, the further all his other desires recede into the background. Wealth, power, sexual gratification—all these become meaningless; a glass of water acquires more importance and offers greater promise of happiness than anything else in the world. The stimulus threshold of the predominant instinct has dropped to zero, and all the other members of the parliament of instincts slump helplessly in their seats. The body exclusively obeys the directives of the one overpowering instinct: thirst. Then the unfortunate man reaches an oasis and, in a positive frenzy of delight, drinks his fill. The stimulus threshold climbs again, and hunger and sleep now stake their claim. The next day the man's interest in other things revives. Various other members of the parliament of instincts rise to speak.

Swallowing liquid no longer induces an ecstasy of happiness, and within a few days drinking has become just as natural and just as much a part of normal routine as it ever was.

One more example: A man has decided to acquire a house and strains to attain his objective. In this case the responsible member of parliament is a structure formed by the imagination. This instinct, too, thrusts its fellow instincts into the background and soon controls the mind and, consequently, the actions of the man in question. This is another instance where a stimulus threshold has sunk, creating an appetency. The man duly succeeds in acquiring his house. He moves in, ecstatically happy. Weeks and months pass, and still the house brings him joy and happiness—though other desires assert themselves in the meantime. First, the man's thoughts turn to a car. Eventually he becomes a millionaire. Now that every wish is fulfilled almost before it finds expression, all the man's instincts undergo a raising of the stimulus threshold until only supernormally strong stimuli can elicit feelings of happiness. In the end, the "poor" rich man does not know what to wish for any longer. Then fortune deserts him, and he loses everything. He falls sick; his friends ignore him. And, lo and behold, he suddenly derives happiness from insignificant little trifles. A bird alights on the ground near him, he throws it a few crumbs, the bird pecks at them—and tears come into the man's eyes. His thoughts return to the house. What a magnificent property it was! And the good health which he always took for granted—what a blessing that was! As soon as something is taken for granted, the stimulus threshold rises; starve a little, and it drops. Thus the real enemy of human happiness is not unhappiness but satiation and the familiarity that breeds contempt.

Prosperous parents often make the mistake of fulfilling all their children's numerous wishes as promptly as possible, simply because they can afford to and because they imagine that they are thereby guaranteeing them a particularly happy childhood. They are not, in fact, doing them any real favor. The children become restive, refractory, and hard to please. The explanation is simple: They yearn for feelings of happiness, but these are linked with appetencies which take shape only when they are correspondingly hard of fulfillment. In this respect, children of less prosperous parents actually have an advantage.

The phenomenon of varying stimulus thresholds may be the basis of the only natural justice in the world. The poor, whether young or old, can experience feelings of happiness quite as intense as those of the rich, if not more so. Furthermore, the commonly expressed theory that moderation is a good basis for happiness finds very real confirmation in this. Anyone with enough strength of mind not to pamper himself can hold down his stimulus thresholds artificially; his various urges will then bring him feelings of happiness in response to moderate stimuli —and moderate stimuli are, from a practical point of view, easier to attain than supernormal. He who abstains obtains, said Lao-tse, and it is doubtful if the facts could be stated more succinctly. The Epicurean school of philosphy, which also grasped this truth, went so far as to recommend moderate asceticism as a means of whetting, rather than blunting, the instincts. Anyone who breaks habits and intersperses his normal existence with spells of simple living will obtain similar results.

Excitatory processes occasioned by conflict situations are disagreeable to man. These occur when instincts collide with each other or with deliberately formed intentions, or when an action considered to be important encounters unexpected difficulties which call for a swift decision. In earlier times, when large sections of the world's population were still deprived and oppressed, the feelings of those with no hope of advancement consisted solely of such conflict situations. Their urges found no satisfactory outlet, and life dragged on from one privation and humiliation to the next, beset by disease and physical hardship. This situation accounted for Buddhism, which sees our present existence as a vale of sorrow—in other words, something negative—and preaches total suppression of wishes and desires as the sole way out. Total extinction here becomes the goal of earthly existence. Because urges can be gradually weakened by nonfulfillment, this method certainly affords relief. To revert to our earlier metaphor, the horses pulling the cart are no longer fed or watered—in fact, everything possible is done to kill them off. No new uges are formed by habit in such a situation, and the imagination is similarly reduced to a state of desirelessness. This deliberate blunting of desire and consequent inner independence produced a condition of fatalistic equanimity which was more satisfying than the earlier state of affairs. Christianity, which originated under similar conditions, went a stage further. This doctrine also sees life as a vale of tears, but it is only an ordeal or transitional phase. Happy are the unhappy, for theirs shall be everlasting bliss. This attitude produces a negative effect too, but it is more positively happy than Buddhism. Never, perhaps, has the power of human imagination been more rigorously tested than by Christianity. As a formula for living, it succeeded in doing something which is probably incapable of improvement: It succeeded in making the sufferer rejoice in his suffering, the downtrodden in his oppression, the helpless in his impotence.

Science also has something definite to say about the extent to which material possessions can bring happiness. Those things which we call possessions—disregarding food and territorial claims (landed property)—are artificial organs in the fullest sense. Each of these functional structures is, as we have already said, associated with a need to form acquired coordinations appropriate to their use. Other requirements are that they should be maintained, regulated, and tended when necessary. Thus, like every integral physical organ, these units make certain demands, and their possession creates an appetency to use them—especially where larger and less easily procurable contrivances are concerned. A bought but unused pencil may be forgotten without more ado; a dress may oblige a woman to wear it, and a car may very well become master instead of servant by compelling its owner to use it. Diogenes and his followers freed themselves from such fetters—from such an influencing of the will—by roaming the countryside with nothing but a blanket and a begging bag, and many modern hoboes and dropouts behave similarly. It goes without saying that such a mode of life is suited only to individuals, not to an entire population. A very real problem does exist here, however, particularly for the wealthy and well endowed. They may easily surround themselves with more artificial organs than their central nervous system can master successfully; they may be presented with too many opportunities and too many consequent obligations. If a man augments his organizational system with too much property, with too many atificially acquired organs, time becomes too short for him to exploit all the opportunities they offer, and they turn against him. They make certain demands on him, coercing, compelling, tempting; the controlling cerebral structures war against one another and make the man restless and discontented despite his wealth. Once again a certain measure of restraint provides the basis of happiness. Individuals certainly vary in their ability to cope successfully with material possessions. As long as they are seen as something wholly separate from ourselves, there is no reason why constant accretions of property should not enhance our capacity for happiness. If, on the other hand, they are treated as supplementary functional units which make the same demands on the central nervous system as our bodily organs proper, it is easy to see that there can be too much of a good thing, that the "body" eventually becomes distended and overburdened, and that the functional units—each in itself capable of arousing feelings of happiness—neutralize and erode one another.

There is one more danger associated with property. Pomp and riches can, as the Koran says, easily become "barren and withered, and turn at last to parched stubble," and Thucydides wrote, "Woe to him who loses a happiness to which he was accustomed." As happens when we lose a person whom we have loved or grown accustomed to, hundreds of cerebral "tracks" run off into the void, must be disentangled, rerouted, and adapted to changed circumstances. The urges activated by former habits have to be killed off. There seems little doubt that much depends here, too, upon the way in which the driver of the cart handles his reins. If we are modest from the start, if we overlay our existing ties with a fatalistic conception of just how ephemeral they can be, and if we do not make them a basis for overambitious dreams of the future, two advantages are gained: We hold our stimulus threshold down by never taking the moment for granted; and we are prepared for a potential loss. Although this certainly entails a renunciation of paradisal unconcern, such is the trend that characterizes our development into human beings.

In the modern free-enterprise world, man's acquisitive urge

is artificially stimulated. Because of the vastly increased range of goods and services designed to bring happiness, alluring possibilities have become almost too numerous. The resulting burdens, fatigue, and nervousness can be observed with particular clarity in metropolitan cities. The modern world resembles Goethe's sorcerer's apprentice, who conjured up a spirit from which he could not escape. Each new consumer good, every novel form of enjoyment and pleasure, acquires a sort of independent existence, makes demands on people, tempts them, and fights—in a sense—for its life, simply because of background commercial interests which do all in their power to "sell." In Communist countries private ownership is restricted or entirely banned by the state, which inhibits personal aggrandizement and development on the part of the individual.

Modern humanity now directs its gaze with interest—and anxiety—toward East and West in turn, under the impression that man's future lies in one quarter or the other. The ideas developed in this book indicate that it lies in neither, and that both trends are exaggerated.

That Communism is not a system qualified to become the final stage of human development may be inferred from the considerations that follow. Let us assume that Communist doctrine were to conquer the entire world. What then? The absorption of individual creatures into a superordinate power structure is biologically significant in that a stronger productive system comes into being—stronger, however, only in regard to rivals and enemies. What would remain to justify the existence of such a system if it ruled the world in splendid isolation? It would then—if consistently true to its basic principles—serve to *prevent* the efficient from developing and to *enforce* a state of affairs in which all its human components were permitted, on principle, to lead strictly similar lives with strictly limited organs and strictly controlled joys and sorrows. But that would be a condition so diametrically opposed to the general evolutionary trend that the system would disintegrate of its own accord as soon as its victory was complete. And, once again, mankind would be confronted by the question: What now?

A system of government probably better qualified to become worldwide would be one that on principle guaranteed the rights of very different systems. The suppression of individual groups —a process which summoned Communism and other movements into being—cannot be justified and has since been eliminated in another way. What must also be eliminated, however, is the idea that one way of life is equally suited to all men. This is as untrue as it would be to assert that the same rules of conduct produce identical results in individual cases. Individuals differ widely, if only in the formation of their instincts, and this is a source of wealth which should not be dispensed with. Lack of tolerance toward other schools of thought is, perhaps, the one *acquired* characteristic which might genuinely be described as evil. The inhabitants of our tiny planet may all be in the same boat, but this does not mean that each passenger is identical. Human beings do not possess the same inherited characteristics, the same talents, the same vitality, the same desires. The notion that they are equal is fundamentally wrong. What is right, on the other hand, is that we ought to grant each human being certain equal basic rights—coupled, of course, with equal basic obligations. How the individual develops—within the framework of an overall system required by all—ought surely to be his own affair. On this level, no one way is essentially better or worse than another.

The development of modern free enterprise is similarly exaggerated. All progress, every spatiotemporal structure which serves us in any way, is undoubtedly good in itself, but only for as long as it really serves us and does not succeed in making us its servants. Today, spurred on by the quest for markets, the general tendency is to influence the individual in such a way that he does more and wants more than is compatible with his time and energy. Buyers are, by definition, dissatisfied, so everything is done to create dissatisfaction. One particularly bad—and biologically stupid—tendency is to depreciate that which exists. Whatever it may look like, the artificial organ becomes, by reason of its acquisition, a part of our physical organization and itself acquires value because of that (but only that). Influences which cause us to slough it off for no good reason and seek an endless succession of replacements are necessarily harmful to us, undermine our self-confidence and natural basis of existence.

The central evil in this development consists in playing up a social criterion based on the ownership of purchasable commodities. As long as our neighbor's possessions determine the value to us of what we ourselves own, we are merely puppets on a string. The quest for market outlets has destroyed many values within a very short time. Festivals—one of the staples of human civilization—are increasingly becoming dates on which people can be persuaded to buy things or exchange presents—in other words, to acquire goods and services. Works of art are blithely linked with articles offered for sale and thereby forfeit their elicitive power. The same pernicious tendency is clearly discernible in many other fields. Inoculation with too many wants causes us to work more than we wish, have less time for reflection, less power of resistance, and a greater susceptibility to sales influences. Such is the prevailing nexus of cause and effect.

The underdeveloped countries lie in a no-man's-land between the two main spheres of influence. They are wooed by both camps, but not in their own best interests. One side aims to incorporate them in its power complex and turn them into functional units; the other to implant new desires and a new sense of values so as to convert them into a seller's market. Their original self-assurance—as valid as any other—is being undermined from both sides. Something primitive, perhaps, but rooted in itself is thus being transformed into something second- or third-rate: an industrious cog in a machine or an industrious member of a herd of buyers.

Epilogue

THIS book began by describing a new method of cinematography designed to objectivize human behavior and shed light on behavior structures which we normally fail to see or ignore, either because the sight of human beings is too familiar to us or because the processes involved are too slow or too rapid for our powers of observation. This method must surely have many other fields of application, *e.g.*, psychiatry, work study, and traffic research. It would be particularly desirable if the same technique were admitted to the field of ethnological research as well. Primitive peoples still possess original customs, original handicrafts, and original forms of community life, but at the present rate of development it will not be long before they all become things of the past. The motor patterns associated with them ought, while they are still observable, to be recorded in the form of accelerated long shots and slow-motion close-ups. Films of this type represent documentary records of authentic and uninfluenced procedures and could supply valuable instruction to later generations of investigators pursuing problems which may, in a hundred years' time, present quite another appearance. Almost all such sequences hitherto recorded on film have been especially set up for the occasion. These possess value too, of course, but only when unobtrusively filmed records of the same procedures also exist.

In view of the material presented here and the considerations

arising therefrom, it is hoped that scientifically directed research into human behavior has been shown to be valid and
meaningful. To view things from this angle is not, repeat not,
to depreciate human beings or impugn their uniqueness and
dignity. Nothing they may have achieved and produced loses
one whit by being viewed from the aspect of nature and evolution; on the contrary, this mode of examination actually
throws our human peculiarities into sharper relief. Now that
no further doubt attaches to our ancestry—and here lies the
crucial point which has simply failed to penetrate the consciousness of human society in general—it is time to form conclusions in regard to self-assessment. We shall cope with our manifold problems, in particular the vast problem of war or peace,
only if we know more about the workings of nature within
us, if we isolate the phenomena in human behavior which still
link us with our animal past, distinguish what is innate and
uncontrollable in us, and discover how we can operate on these
mechanisms with our conscious ego. Psychologists, who have always made man the starting point of their inquiries, have produced valuable results in this way. The plain fact is, however,
that in the present state of knowledge another starting point
would be more natural and correct. If we want to understand
the latest and most complicated link in the long evolutionary
chain, it is expedient to base individual inquiries upon the
modest beginnings of that chain.

Problems of child education and upbringing are particularly
affected by this line of research. Until now, the developing human being has been equipped for life with every conceivable
form of information save one: self-knowledge. How does our
mysterious ego take shape, and what are the details of its composition? What forces operate within us, how do they manifest
themselves, and how can we best make use of them under prevailing circumstances? How do we behave toward other people, notably our partners in sex, how do the latter react, and
how can we arrive at a harmonious relationship? And, finally,
how can we build a fruitful life in full awareness of our own
potentials and limitations?

Modern educators still tend to present earlier generations as
paragons, existing institutions as right and good, existing schools

of thought as more or less correct. Discipline may require this to a certain extent, but when a developing individual has attained a degree of maturity, it is surely only fair to draw his or her attention to the relativity of good and evil, the relative value of various systems, the relative truth of current beliefs. The overwhelming majority of people need suitable leadership and suitable examples, true, but this makes it all the more important to develop a critical appreciation of how far a leader should be trusted and how far an example merits imitation. If man wishes to develop still further, children must be regarded not as artificial organs belonging to parents or society but as developing individuals worthy of respect. The older generation should step down from its pedestal. Young people must be acquainted with past achievements, but these should speak for themselves. The educating generation should muster the courage to promote genuinely free development, even at the risk of breeding opposition to its own beliefs. If the avoidable tensions in this world are to be diminished, this is the only road to take.

A Babylonian confusion of languages reigns in the sciences which concern themselves with man. Countless conceptual systems have been constructed in accordance with a diversity of viewpoints, each fully consistent in itself but none compatible with the rest. The practical effect of this is that the same words are associated with different concepts, a circumstance which necessarily leads to pointless controversy and time-wasting misunderstandings. People have become gravely infected with a resigned belief that this state of affairs is more or less inevitable, that the phenomenon is a simple consequence of the scope of the subject and the necessity for specialization. This may have been true while no neutral system of reference existed, for each school of thought could with equal justification claim that its own mode of definition was the best and most correct. Ever since the nature of our ancestry was proved, however, a natural and neutral system of reference has existed, namely, the development of life. Just as each new structure and each new phenomenon has proceeded from it, so the conceptual systems of all specialized sciences ought to go back to the common source of that development. This book has sought to show how a conceptual bridge of this kind can be built, *e.g.*, to political science, economics, and aesthetics. It remains to be seen whether this line of thought can be pursued further, but even if it proves to be a dead end, nothing can detract from the demand that such bridges should be sought. As much as fifty years ago, the Russian economist Bogdanov and the German sociologist Plenge—proceeding from different viewpoints—endeavored to found a school of general organizational research. They never realized their ideal, which was a system of reference embracing all the sciences. Today comparative behavioral research provides the natural basis for such a system of reference. Many concepts in this branch of biology will have to be reformulated for the benefit of this wider objective in a clearer and more universally applicable way, but the concepts developed from the study of animal behavior do, necessarily, constitute the point of departure.

Are we at all capable of wanting what we want? Our free will is subject to still another limitation imposed upon it by the concepts which we ourselves have evolved and labeled with verbal designations. It is all too easy to forget that these concepts are the highly personal work of man, and that this does not necessarily make them a mirror of reality. They are pigeonholes in which we file a multiplicity of phenomena so as to help us survey, ponder, and express them. This is how human evolution began. In the beginning was "the word"—or, more precisely, the concept furnished with a verbal designation. These "pigeonholes," which are transmitted from one brain to another by way of upbringing and tradition, encourage us to believe that the phenomena contained by them belong together naturally—in other words, that these units are realities which actually exist in the world. They are not. Each concept or term is merely a useful device, a mental tool. Each of them, when provided with a verbal symbol, is a useful functional unit and, in that sense, another form of acquired or artificial organ. Once again, there is a danger that servants will become masters, that these filing systems will cease to serve our purposes and compress our thoughts into their own mold. We have now reached the very stage at which it might be expedient to submit this master-servant relationship to critical scrutiny. However long and faithfully it may have served us, a concept which no longer does its job has no right to impede us further. We must discard it, like any tool that has ceased to be useful.

Nothing can be more important to a young scientist than the realization that words are not to be trusted. We need them and could not think without them, but they must be handled with the utmost caution. They restrict our freedom of thought and lead our wishes by the hand. Once a brain has employed certain concepts for twenty or thirty years it is scarcely in a position to part with them, and once they have propagated themselves for generations they acquire the stability of a firmly rooted tree. The young and developing brain is still free and untrammeled in this respect. It can put each such servant to the test before committing itself.

Appendices

Key to Sources

The first two figures indicate page number and line, the following figure or figures refer to the Bibliography. For example, if it is required to discover the source of particulars given on page 14, line 15, the ensuing figure 34 refers to a work listed in the Bibliography. A few references to relevant works not mentioned in the text are also given in this way.

9/ 4 = 111	28/37 = 120	37/15 = 48
13/22 = 33, 34	31/20 = 35	37/19 = 146
18/ 3 = 55	31/22 = 15	37/30 = 97, 103
19/ 1 = 170	31/24 = 142	38/ 5 = 30
20/23 = 97, 98	31/27 = 133	38/13 = 33, 34
25/ 6 = 66	31/30 = 83, 33	38/19 = 99
25/ 9 = 163	31/33 = 47	38/38 = 132, 33, 34
25/12 = 118	32/ 5 = 28, 31	39/31 = 166
25/13 = 66, 134, 19	32/16 = 26	41/ 1 = 120
26/ 3 = 53	32/31 = 160	41/24 = 94
26/11 = 17, 44	32/37 = 115	42/ 7 = 103
26/18 = 108	33/ 1 = 84	42/24 = 35
26/20 = 43, 90	33/ 7 = 139	42/28 = 27, 33
26/21 = 73	34/ 6 = 93	42/33 = 32, 168
26/22 = 136	34/37 = 156	43/ 2 = 33, 34
26/23 = 7, 85	35/10 = 143, 144	43/13 = 150, 124
26/24 = 93, 96	35/24 = 79	43/21 = 33, 34
26/27 = 36	35/27 = 158	43/31 = 103
26/28 = 38	35/31 = 161	44/ 1 = 97
26/39 = 5	35/34 = 105	44/21 = 157
27/32 = 32	36/ 1 = 33, 34	45/ 9 = 88
28/24 = 59—63	36/ 6 = 50, 86	46/ 1 = 65

46/14 = 116
46/29 = 89
46/39 = 157
47/16 = 65
49/15 = 117
49/27 = 155
49/32 = 65, 145
49/35 = 96, 101, 102
50/ 3 = 3
50/12 = 95, 97, 98
50/34 = 164
52/17 = 129
52/28 = 25
52/34 = 109, 8
53/ 4 = 70, 4
53/ 9 = 16
53/10 = 12
53/13 = 56
53/19 = 14
53/20 = 1
53/24 = 46
53/33 = 28, 31
53/38 = 32
54/ 2 = 159
54/ 5 = 106
54/18 = 158
54/27 = 32
54/32 = 112
55/ 3 = 158
55/ 6 = 151
55/10 = 39
55/16 = 71, 72
56/24 = 147
56/30 = 82
57/ 1 = 130
57/ 2 = 131
58/ 5 = 74, 75, 77, 78
58/23 = 76
58/31 = 80
58/34 = 50
60/ 5 = 129
60/38 = 120
61/14 = 57
62/22 = 32
63/ 3 = 152—154

63/12 = 114
63/14 = 33, 34
63/17 = 93
63/24 = 158
63/34 = 58
64/11 = 140, 141
64/16 = 92, 93
64/22 = 100
64/29 = 113
64/37 = 100
65/ 4 = 67
65/11 = 54
65/15 = 107
67/23 = 51
68/28 = 95, 97, 98
69/11 = 64
70/25 = 122
71/33 = 97
73/ 6 = 97, 98
73/22 = 97, 98
73/38 = 95, 97, 98
74/38 = 116
75/11 = 33, 167
75/32 = 103
76/ 8 = 103
89/18 = 98
91/17 = 33, 34
91/36 = 27
92/ 7 = 33, 34
92/17 = 98
93/ 5 = 80, 27
93/23 = 45
94/18 = 6
94/31 = 33, 34
94/34 = 110
95/ 3 = 98
95/26 = 98
95/27 = 45
95/36 = 98
95/39 = 10, 111
96/33 = 98
98/ 1 = 98
98/16 = 45
98/31 = 80
102/28 = 128
108/22 = 98

108/26 = 81
108/35 = 101
110/ 2 = 87
111/18 = 21
112/ 3 = 99
112/ 6 = 29
113/12 = 99
113/39 = 21
115/34 = 21
116/15 = 33
120/13 = 103
121/19 = 33, 167
121/29 = 139
121/34 = 97
123/39 = 2, 11, 33, 34, 103
124/ 9 = 33, 34
124/19 = 158
124/27 = 162
124/31 = 97, 103
125/ 4 = 103
125/11 = 103
125/21 = 33
125/28 = 21
127/ 3 = 33, 34
127/ 5 = 2
129/ 4 = 21
129/29 = 21
130/31 = 21
138/10 = 138, 126, 125, 22, 137, 135
144/15 = 50, 86
144/37 = 33, 34
147/13 = 21
156/38 = 20, 169
162/23 = 93, 58
163/ 1 = 158
163/ 4 = 140, 141
163/ 8 = 100
163/27 = 37
164/ 2 = 148, 149, 13, 24
164/23 = 121
165/12 = 33, 34
166/ 4 = 24
167/ 2 = 42

168/ 7 = 52, 153
168/ 9 = 58, 93
170/ 1 = 23
170/16 = 42
173/27 = 34, 111

183/18 = 119
187/12 = 40
187/14 = 45
188/ 2 = 131
188/ 8 = 65

188/21 = 80
194/22 = 45
197/21 = 18, 98, 103
203/20 = 98
218/ 6 = 9, 123

Abbreviations of Sources in Bibliography

Am. Zool. = American Zoologist
Arch. Kinderheilkunde = Archiv für Kinderheilkunde
Beitr. Fortpfl. biol. Vögel = Beiträge zur Fortpflanzungsbiologie der Vögel
Biol. Lect. Mar. Biol. Lab. Woods Hole = Biological Lectures of the Marine Biological Laboratory, Woods Hole
Brit. Birds = British Birds
Bull. Am. Mus. Nat. Hist. = Bulletin of the American Museum of Natural History
Cambr. Monogr. in Exp. Biol. = Cambridge Monographs in Experimental Biology
Comp. Psychol. Monogr. = Comparative Psychological Monographs
Die Naturwiss. = Die Naturwissenschaften
Erg. Psychol. = Ergebnisse der Psychologie
Fol. primat. = Folia primatologica
Genet. Psychol. Monogr. = Genetical Psychological Monograph
Groups Proc. Jos. Macy Found. = Groups Processes Josiah Macy Foundation
J. Child Psychol. Psychiatr. = Journal of Child Psychology and Psychiatry
J. Gen. Psychol. = Journal of General Psychology
J. Neuropsychiatry = Journal of Neuropsychiatry
J. Ornith. = Journal für Ornithologie
J. Psychol. = Journal of Psychology
Nat. Geogr. Mag. = National Geographic Magazine
Nat. Hist. = Natural History
Naturw. Rundschau = Naturwissenschaftliche Rundschau
Pflüg. Arch. = Pflügers Archiv für die gesamte Physiologie der Menschen und der Tiere

Psychol. Forschg. = Psychologische Forschung
Psychol. Rev. = Psychological Review
Scient. Americ. = Scientific American
Stud. Gen. = Studium Generale
Tijdschr. Ent. = Tijdschrift voor entomologie
Verh. D. Zool. Ges. Tübingen Zool. Anz. = Verhandlungen der Zoologischen Gesellschaft Tübingen, Zoologischer Anzeiger
Wils. Bull. = The Wilson Bulletin
Z. angew. Psychol. u. Charakterk. = Zeitschrift für Psychologie. Mit Zeitschrift für angewandte Psychologie und Charakterkunde
Z. Morphol. Ökol. Tiere = Zeitschrift für Morphologie und Ökologie der Tiere
Z. Tierpsychol. = Zeitschrift für Tierpsychologie
Z. vgl. Physiol. = Zeitschrift für vergleichende Physiologie
Zool. Anz. Suppl. = Zoologischer Anzeiger Supplement (Verhandlungen der Zoologischen Gesellschaft Tübingen)
Zool. Jb. = Zoologisches Jahrbuch

Bibliography

Part One of this book is based largely on the research of Eibl-Eibesfeldt as contained in source 33 below. The reader interested in more detailed particulars of behavioral research should consult the expanded treatment in source 34. Source 104 presents a summary of most of Lorenz's works. Special attention is also drawn to sources 98 (contained in 104) and 103.

1. Agranoff, B. W., "Memory and Protein Synthesis." *Scient. Americ.*, 216 (6):115–23,, 1967.
2. Ambrose, J. A., "The Age of Onset of Ambivalence in Early Infancy: Indications from the Study of Laughing." *J. Child Psychol. Psychiatr.*, 4:167–81, 1963.
3. Antonius, O., "Über Symbolhandlungen und Verwandtes bei Säugetieren." *Z. Tierpsychol.*, 3:263–78, 1939.
4. Babich, F. R., *et al.*, "Transfer of a Response to Naïve Rats by Injection of Ribonucleic Acid Extracted from Trained Rats." *Science*, 149:656–57, 1965.
5. Baerends, G. P., "Fortpflanzungsverhalten und Orientierung der Grabwespe, *Ammophila campestris.*" *Tijdschr. Ent.*, 84:68–275, 1941.
6. Bally, G., *Vom Ursprung und von den Grenzen der Freiheit. Eine Deutung des Spieles bei Tier und Mensch.* Basel, Birkhaeuser, 1945.
7. Beach, F. A., "Comparison of Copulatory Behavior of Male Rats Raised in Isolation, Cohabitation and Segregation." *J. Gen. Psychol.*, 60:121–36, 1942.
8. Best, J. B., "Protopsychology." *Scient. Americ.*, 208 (2):55–62, 1963.
9. Bogdanov, A., *Allgemeine Organisationslehre.* Berlin, Organisation Verlag, 1926.
10. Bolk, L., *Das Problem der Menschwerdung.* Jena, 1926.

11. Bolwig, N., "Facial Expression in Primates with Remarks on Parallel Development in Certain Carnivores." *Behaviour*, 22:167–92, 1964.
12. Bonner, J., "The Molecular Biology of Memory." Summary of the Symposium on the Role of Macromolecules in Complex Behavior, Kansas State University, pp. 89–95, 1964.
13. Bowlby, J., "Maternal Care and Mental Health." World Health Organization. Monogr. Ser. 2, 1952.
14. Boycott, B., "Learning in the Octopus." *Scient. Americ.*, 212 (3):42–50, 1965.
15. Bullock, T. H., "Predator Recognition and Escape Responses of Some Intertidal Gastropods in the Presence of Starfish." *Behaviour*, 5:130–40, 1953.
16. Byrne, W. L., *et al.*, "Memory Transfer." *Science*, 153:658–59, 1966.
17. Carmichael, L., "The Development of Behavior in Vertebrates, Experimentally Removed from the Influence of External Stimulation." *Psychol. Rev.*, 33:51–58, 1926.
18. Carpenter, C. R., "Societies of Monkeys and Apes." *Biol. Symp.*, 8:177–204, 1942.
19. Clark, E., *et. al.*, "Mating Behavior Patterns in Two Sympatric Species of Xiphophorian Fishes: Their Inheritance and Significance in Sexual Isolation." *Bull. Am. Mus. Nat. Hist.*, 103:135–226, 1954.
20. Cowles, J. T., "Food-Tokens as Incentives for Learning by Chimpanzees." *Comp. Psychol. Monogr.*, 14:1–96, 1937.
21. Darwin, C., *The Expression of Emotions in Man and Animals.* London, 1872.
22. De Vore, I., *Primate Behavior: Field Studies of Monkeys and Apes.* New York, Holt, Rinehart & Winston, 1965.
23. Dollard, J., *et al., Frustration and Aggression.* New Haven, Yale University Press, 1939.
24. Dührssen, A., *Psychogene Erkrankungen bei Kindern und Jugendlichen.* Göttingen, Verl. f. med. Psychol., 1960.
25. Eccles, J. C., *The Neurophysiological Basis of Mind: The Principles of Neurophysiology.* London, Oxford University Press, 1953.
26. Eibl-Eibesfeldt, I., "Ein Beitrag zur Paarungsbiologie der Erdkröte *(Bufo bufo L.)*." *Behaviour*, 2:217–36, 1950.
27. Eibl-Eibesfeldt, I., "Über die Jugendentwicklung des Verhaltens eines männlichen Dachses *(Meles meles* L.) unter besonderer Berücksichtigung des Spieles." *Z. Tierpsychol.*, 7:327–55, 1950.
28. Eibl-Eibesfeldt, I., "Nahrungserwerb und Beuteschema der Erdkröte *(Bufo bufo L.)*." *Behaviour*, 4:1–35, 1951.
29. Eibl-Eibesfeldt, I., "Über Symbiosen, Parasitismus und andere zwischenartliche Beziehungen bei tropischen Meeresfischen." *Z. Tierpsychol.*, 12:203–19, 1955.
30. Eibl-Eibesfeldt, I., "Der Kommentkampf der Meerechse (Bell: *Amblyrhynchus cristatus*) nebst einigen Notizen zur Biologie dieser Art." *Z. Tierpsychol.*, 12:49–62, 1955.

31. Eibl-Eibesfeldt, I., "Die Verhaltensentwicklung des Scheibenzünglers (*Discoglossus pictus*) unter besonderer Berücksichtigung der Beutefanghandlungen. *Z. Tierpsychol.*, 19:385–93, 1962.

32. Eibl-Eibesfeldt, I., "Angeborenes und Erworbenes im Verhalten einiger Säuger." *Z. Tierpsychol.*, 20:705–54, 1963.

33. Eibl-Eibesfeldt, I., "Ethologie, die Biologie des Verhaltens," in *Handbuch der Biologie* (Frankfurt, Athenaion, 1966), 2:341–559.

34. Eibl-Eibesfeldt, I., *Ethology: The Biology of Behavior*. New York, Holt, Rinehart & Winston, 1970.

35. Eibl-Eibesfeldt, I., and Hass, H. "Erfahrungen mit Haien." *Z. Tierpsychol.*, 16:733–46, 1959.

36. Eibl-Eibesfeldt, I., and Hass, H., "Neue Wege der Humanethologie." *Homo*, 18:13–23, 1967.

37. Erikson, E. H., *Wachstum und Krisen der gesunden Persönlichkeit*. Stuttgart, Klett, 1953.

38. Fabré, J. H., *Souvenir entomologique*. Paris, Delagrave, 1879–1910.

39. Fisher, J., and Hinde, R., "The Opening of Milk Bottles by Birds." *Brit. Birds*, 42:347–58, 1949.

40. Fleugge, J., *Die Entfaltung der Anschauungskraft. Ein Beitrag zur pädagogischen Anthropologie*. Heidelberg, 1963.

41. Freedman, D., "An Ethological Approach to the Genetic Study of Human Behavior," in St. G. Vandenberg, *Method and Goals in Human Behavior Genetics* (New York and London, Academic Press, 1965), pp. 141–61.

42. Freud, S., *Collected Works*. London, Imago Publ., 1950.

43. Frisch, K. v., *Die Tanzsprache und Orientierung der Bienen*. Berlin and Heidelberg, Springer, 1965.

44. Fromme, A., "An Experimental Study of the Factors of Maturation and Practise in Behavioral Development of the Frog *Rana pipiens*." *Genet. Psychol. Monogr.*, 24:219–61, 1941.

45. Gehlen, A., *Der Mensch. Seine Natur und seine Stellung in der Welt*. Berlin, 1940.

46. Gerard, R. W., "The Fixation of Experience," in J. F. Delafresnaye, *Brain Mechanisms and Learning* (Oxford, Blackwell, 1961), pp. 21–35.

47. Gibson, E. J., and Walk, R. D., "The Visual Cliff." *Scient. Americ.*, 202 (4):64–71, 1960.

48. Gillard, E. Th., "The Evolution of Bowerbirds." *Scient. Americ.*, 209 (2):38–46, 1963.

49. Goodall, J., "My Life Among Wild Chimpanzees." *Nat. Geogr. Mag.*, 125 (8):272–308, 1963.

50. Goodall, J., "Chimpanzees of the Gombe Stream Reserve," in I. De Vore, *Primate Behavior* (New York, Holt, Rinehart & Winston, 1965), pp. 425–73.

51. Gossen, H. H., *Entwicklung und Gesetze des menschlichen Verkehrs und der daraus fliessenden Regeln für menschliches Handeln*. Braunschweig, 1854.

52. Gray, P. H., "Theory and Evidence of Imprinting in Human Infants." *J. Psychol.*, 46:155–60, 1958.

53. Grohmann, J., "Modifikation oder Funktionsreifung?" *Z. Tierpsychol.*, 2:132–44, 1939.

54. Harlow, H. F., and Harlow, M. K., "Social Deprivation in Monkeys." *Scient. Americ.*, 207:137–46, 1962.

55. Heberer, G., *Die Evolution der Organismen*. Stuttgart, G. Fischer, 1967.

56. Hering, E., *Über das Gedächtnis als allgemeine Funktion der organisierten Materie*, 3d ed. Leipzig, Akademische Verlags Gesellschaft, 1921.

57. Hess, E. H., "Space Perception in the Chick." *Scient. Americ.*, 195:71–80, 1956.

58. Hess, E. H., "Imprinting, an Effect of Early Experience." *Science*, 130:133–41, 1959.

59. Holst, E. v., "Über den Prozess der zentralen Koordination." *Pflüg. Arch.*, 236:149–58, 1935.

60. Holst, E. v., "Versuche zur Theorie der relativen Koordination." *Pflüg. Arch.*, 237:93–121, 1936.

61. Holst, E. v., "Untersuchungen über die Funktion des Zentralnervensystems beim Regenwurm." *Zool. Jb.*, 51:547–88, 1937.

62. Holst, E. v., "Weitere Versuche zum nervösen Mechanismus der Bewegung beim Regenwurm." *Zool. Jb.*, 53:68–100, 1939.

63. Holst, E. v., "Die relative Koordination als Phänomen und als Methode zentralnervöser Funktionsanalyse." *Erg. Psychol.*, 42:228–303, 1939.

64. Holst, E. v., and Mittelstaedt, H., "Das Reafferenz-Prinzip." *Die Naturwiss.*, 37:464–76, 1950.

65. Holst, E. v., and Saint-Paul, U. v., "Vom Wirkungsgefüge der Triebe." *Die Naturwiss.*, 18:409–22, 1960.

66. Hörmann-Heck, S. v., "Untersuchungen über den Erbgang einiger Verhaltensweisen bei Grillenbastarden (*Gryllus campestris x Gryllus bimaculatus*)." *Z. Tierpsychol.*, 14:137–83, 1957.

67. Immelmann, K., "Prägungserscheinungen in der Gesangsentwicklung junger Zebrafinken." *Die Naturwiss.*, 52:169–70, 1965.

68. Immelmann, K., "Zur Irreversibilität der Prägung." *Die Naturwiss.*, 53:209, 1966.

69. Immelmann, K., "Zur ontogenetischen Gesangsentwicklung bei Prachtfinken." *Zool. Anz. Suppl.*, 30:320–32, 1967.

70. Jacobson, A. L., *et al.*, "Differential Approach Tendencies Produced by Injection of RNA from Trained Rats." *Science*, 150:636–37, 1965.

71. Kawai, M., "Newly Acquired Pre-Cultural Behavior of the Natural Troop of Japanese Monkeys on Koshima Island." *Primates*, 6:1–30, 1965.

72. Kawamura, S., "The Process of Sub-Cultural Propagation Among Japanese Macaques," in Ch. H. Southwick, *Primate Social Behavior* (New York, Van Nostrand, 1963), pp. 82–90.

73. Klinghammer, E., and Hess, E. H., "Parental Feeding in Ring Doves (*Streptopelia roseogrisea*): Innate or Learned?" *Z. Tierpsychol.*, 21: 338–47, 1964.

74. Koehler, O., " 'Zähl'-Versuche an einem Kolkraben und Vergleichs-versuche an Menschen." *Z. Tierpsychol.*, 5:575–712, 1943.

75. Koehler, O., " 'Zählende' Vögel und vorsprachliches Denken." *Zool. Anz. Suppl.*, 13:129–238, 1949.

76. Koehler, O., *Orientierungsvermögen von Mäusen: Versuche im Hochlabyrinth*. Wiss. Film B 635, Inst. Wiss. Film, Göttingen, 1953.

77. Koehler, O., "Vorbedingungen und Vorstufen unserer Sprache bei Tieren." *Zool. Anz. Suppl.*, 18:327–41, 1954.

78. Koehler, O., *Zählende Vögel und vergleichende Verhaltensforschung*. Congress of Internationl Ornithology, Acta 11, pp. 588–98, 1955.

79. Koehler, O., and Zagarus, A., "Beiträge zum Brutverhalten des Halsbandregenpfeifers (L: *Charadrius hiaticulus*)." *Beitr. Fortpfl. biol. Vögel*, 13:1–9, 1937.

80. Köhler, W., *Intelligenzprüfungen an Menschenaffen*. Berlin, 1921.

81. Kortlandt, A., "Chimpanzees in the Wild." *Scient. Americ.*, 206: 128–38, 1962.

82. Krechevsky, I., " 'Hypotheses' in Rats." *Psychol. Rev.*, 39:516–32, 1932.

83. Krujt, J. P., "Ontogeny of Social Behavior in Burmese Red Jungle Fowl (*Gallus gallus spadiceus*)." *Behaviour*, Suppl. 12, 1958.

84. Lack D., *The Life of the Robin*. Cambridge, Cambridge University Press, 1943.

85. Larsson, K., "Experience and Maturation in the Development of Sexual Behavior in the Male Puberty of Rats." *Behaviour*, 14:101–7, 1959.

86. Lawick-Goodall, J. v., "New Discoveries Among Africa's Chimpanzees." *Nat. Geogr. Mag.*, 128 (6):802–31, 1965.

87. Leakey, L. S. D., "Adventures in the Search of Man." *Nat. Geogr. Mag.*, 123:132–52, 1963.

88. Lehrman, D. S., "The Presence of the Mate and of Nesting Material as Stimuli for the Development of Incubation Behavior and for Gonadotropic Secretion in the Ring Dove." *Endocrinology*, 68:507–16, 1961.

89. Leyhausen, P., Über die Funktion der relativen Stimmungshierarchie (dargestellt am Beispiel der phylogenetischen und ontogenetischen Entwicklung des Beutefanges von Raubtieren)." *Z. Tierpsychol.*, 22:412–94, 1965.

90. Lindauer, M., "Ein Beitrag zur Frage der Arbeitsteilung in Bienenstaat." *Z. vgl. Physiol.*, 34:299–345, 1952.

91. Lindauer, M., *Communication Among Social Bees*. Cambridge, Mass., Harvard University Press, 1961.

92. Lorenz, K., "Beiträge zur Ethologie sozialer Corviden." *J. Ornith.*, 79:67–127, 1931.

93. Lorenz, K., "Der Kumpan in der Umwelt des Vogels." *J. Ornith.*, 83:137–413, 1935.

94. Lorenz, K., "Über die Bildung des Instinktbegriffes." *Die Naturwiss.*, 25:289–300, 307–18, 325–31, 1937.

95. Lorenz, K., "Durch Domestikation verursachte Störungen arteigenen Verhaltens." *Z. angew. Psychol. u. Charakterk.*, 59:2–81, 1940.

96. Lorenz, K., "Vergleichende Bewegungsstudien bei Anatiden." *J. Ornith.*, 89:194–294, 1941.

97. Lorenz, K., "Die angeborenen Formen möglicher Erfahrung." *Z. Tierpsychol.*, 5:235–409, 1943.

98. Lorenz, K., "Ganzheit und Teil in der tierischen und menschlichen Gemeinschaft." *Stud. Gen.*, 3:455–99, 1950.

99. Lorenz, K., "Ausdrucksbewegungen höherer Tiere." *Die Naturwiss.*, 38:113–16, 1951.

100. Lorenz, K., "Morphology and Behavior Patterns in Allied Species." *Group Proc. Jos. Macy Found.*, pp. 168–220, New York, 1954.

101. Lorenz, K., "Psychologie und Stammesgeschichte," in G. Heberer, *Evolution der Organismen* (Stuttgart, G. Fischer, 1959).

102. Lorenz, K., "Phylogenetische Anpassung und adaptive Modifikation des Verhaltens." *Z. Tierpsychol.*, 18:139–87, 1961.

103. Lorenz, K., *On Aggression*. New York, Harcourt, Brace & World, 1966.

104. Lorenz, K., *Über tierisches und menschliches Verhalten. Aus dem Werdegang des Verhaltenslehre* (*Ges. Abhandlg.*), Vols. I and II. Munich, Piper, 1965.

105. Magnus, D., "Zum Problem der 'überoptimalen' Schlüsselreize." *Zool. Anz. Suppl.*, 18:317–25, 1954.

106. Manning, A., "Some Aspects of the Foraging Behaviour of Bumblebees," *Behaviour*, 9:164–201, 1956.

107. Mason, W. A., "The Social Development of Monkeys and Apes," in I. de Vore, *Primate Behavior* (New York, Holt, Rinehart & Winston, 1965), pp. 514–43.

108. Mayer, G., "Untersuchungen über Herstellung und Struktur des Radnetzes von *Aranea diadema* und *Zilla x-notata* mit besonderer Berücksichtigung des Unterschiedes von Jugend- und Altersnetzen." *Z. Tierpsychol.* 9:337–62, 1952.

109. McConnell, J. V., "Memory Transfer Through Cannibalism." *J. Neuropsychiatry*, 3:542–48, 1962.

110. Morris, D., *Biology of Art*. New York, Alfred A. Knopf, 1962.

111. Morris, D., *The Naked Ape*. New York, McGraw-Hill Book Company, 1968.

112. Munn, N. L., *Handbook of Psychological Research on the Rat*. Boston, Houghton Mifflin Company, 1950.

113. Myrberg, A. A., "An Analysis of Preferential Care of Eggs and Young by Adult Cichlid Fishes." *Z. Tierpsychol.*, 21:53–98, 1964.

114. Nicolai, J., "Familientradition in der Gesangstradition des Gimpels (L: *Pyrrhula pyrrhula*)." *J. Ornith.*, 100:39–46, 1959.

115. Noble, G. K., and Bradley, H. T., "The Mating Behavior of Lizards." *Nat. Hist.,* 34:1–15, 1933.

116. Oehlert, B., "Kampf und Paarbildung einiger Cichliden." *Z. Tierpsychol.,* 15:141–74, 1958.

117. Olds, J., "Self-Stimulation of the Brain." *Science,* 127:315–24, 1958.

118. Osche, G., "Die Bedeutung der Osmoregulation und des Winkverhaltens für freilebende Nematoden." *Z. Morphol. Ökol. Tiere,* 41: 54–77, 1952.

119. Packard, V., *The Hidden Persuaders.* New York, David McKay Co., 1957.

120. Pavlov, I. P., *Conditioned Reflexes.* Oxford, 1927.

121. Peiper, A., "Instinkt und angeborenes Schema beim Säugling." *Z. Tierpsychol.,* 8:449–56, 1951.

122. Peiper, A., "Schreit- und Steigbewegungen beim Neugeborenen." *Arch. Kinderheilkde.,* 147:135, 1953.

123. Plenge, J., *Drei Vorlesungen über die allgemeine Organisationslehre.* Essen, Baedeker, 1919.

124. Ploog, D., "Verhaltensforschung und Psychiatrie," in H. W. Gruhle et. al., *Psychiatrie der Gegenwart* (Berlin, Springer, 1964), 1, 1B:291–443.

125. Ploog, D. W., et. al., "Studies on Social and Sexual Behavior in the Squirrel Monkey *(Saimiri scireus)*." *Fol. primat.,* pp. 29–66, 1963.

126. Remane, A., *Das Soziale Leben der Tiere.* Hamburg, Rowohlt 97, 1960.

127. Rensch, B., "Die Abhängigkeit der Struktur und der Leistungen tierischer Gehirne von ihrer Grösse." *Die Naturwiss.,* 45:145–54, 1958.

128. Rensch, B., *Homo Sapiens. Vom Tier zum Halbgott.* Göttingen, Vanderhoeck, 1959.

129. Rensch, B., *Gedächtnis, Abstraktion und Generalisation bei Tieren. Arb. gem, f. Forsch. d. Land. Nordrhein-Westf.* Cologne, Westdeutscher Verlag, 1962.

130. Rensch, B., "Die höchsten Lernleistungen der Tiere." *Naturwiss. Rundschau,* 18:91–101, 1965.

131. Rensch, B., and Dücker, G., "Versuche über visuelle Generalisation bei einer Schleichkatze." *Z. Tierpsychol.,* 16:671–92, 1959.

132. Reuter, O. M., *Lebensgewohnheiten und Instinkte der Insekten.* Berlin, 1913.

133. Roeder, K. D., and Treat, E. A., "The Reception of Bat Cries by the Tympanic Organ of Noctuid Moths," in Rosenblith, *Sensory Communication* (New York, MIT Press and John Wiley, 1961), pp. 545–60.

134. Rothenbuhler, W. C., "Behavior Genetics of Nest Cleaning in Honeybees. IV Responses of F_1 and Backcross Generations to Disease Killed Brood." *Am. Zool.,* 4:111–23, 1964.

135. Sade, D. S., "Determinants of Dominance in a Group of Freeranging Rhesus Monkeys," in S. A. Altman, *Social Communication Among Primates* (Chicago, Chicago University Press, 1967), pp. 99–114.

136. Sauer, F., "Die Entwicklung der Lautäusserungen vom Ei ab schalldicht gehaltener Dorngrasmücken (*Sylvia c. communis* Latham)." *Z. Tierpsychol.* 11:1–93, 1954.

137. Schaller, G. B., *The Mountain Gorilla.* Chicago, Chicago University Press, 1963.

138. Schjelderup-Ebbe, Th., "Social Behavior of Birds," in Murchinson, *A Handbook of Social Psychology.* Pp. 947–72, 1935.

139. Scheidt, W. M., et al., "Störungen der Mutter-Kind-Beziehung bei Truthühnern durch Gehörverlust." *Behaviour,* 16:254–60, 1960.

140. Schutz, F., "Homosexualität und Prägung bei Enten." *Psychol. Forschg.,* 28:439–63, 1965.

141. Schutz, F., "Sexuelle Prägung bei Anatiden." *Z. Tierpsychol.* 22:50–103, 1965.

142. Schwinck, I., "Weitere Untersuchungen zur Frage der Geruchsorientierung der Nachtschmetterlinge: partielle Fühleramputation bei Spinnermännchen, insbesondere des Seidenspinners." *Z. vgl. Physiol.,* 37:439–58, 1955.

143. Seitz, A., "Die Paarbildung bei einigen Zichliden I." *Z. Tierpsychol.,* 4:40–84, 1940.

144. Seitz, A., "Die Paarbildung bei einigen Zichliden II." *Z. Tierpsychol.,* 5:74–101, 1941.

145. Sevenster, P., "A Causal Analysis of a Displacement Activity: Fanning in *Gasterosteus aculeatus.*" *Behaviour,* Suppl. 9, 1961.

146. Sielmann, H., "Filmeinheiten über Laubenvögel," in *Encyclop. Cinematogr.* (Göttingen, Inst. Wiss. Film, 1967), E 1075–78, E 1080–84.

147. Skinner, B. F., *The Behavior of Organisms.* New York, 1938.

148. Spitz, R. A., *Hospitalism. The Psychoanalytic Study of the Child 1.* New York, International Universities Press, 1945.

149. Spitz, R. A., *Anaclitic Depression: An Inquiry into the Genesis of Psychiatric Conditions in Early Childhood. The Psychoanalytic Study of the Child 2.* New York, International Universities Press, 1946.

150. Spitz, R. A., *Die Entstehung der ersten Objektbeziehungen.* Stuttgart, Klett, 1957.

151. Steininger, F., "Zur Soziologie und sonstigen Biologie der Wanderratte." *Z. Tierpsychol.,* 7:356–79, 1950.

152. Thorpe, W. H., "The Learning of Song Patterns by Birds, with Special Reference to the Song of the Chaffinch." *Ibis,* 100:535–70, 1958.

153. Thorpe, W. H., "Sensitive Periods in the Learning of Animals and Men: A Study of Imprinting with Special Reference to the Introduction of Cyclic Behavior," in W. H. Thorpe and O. L. Zangwill, *Current Problems of Animal Behavior* (Cambridge, Mass., Cambridge University Press, 1961), pp. 194–224.

154. Thorpe, W. H., "Bird Song. The Biology of Vocal Communication and Expression in Birds." *Cambridge Monographs in Experimental Biology,* 12, 1961.

155. Tinbergen, N., "Die Übersprungsbewegung." *Z. Tierpsychol.*, 4:1–40, 1940.
156. Tinbergen, N., "Social Releasers and the Experimental Method Required for Their Study." *Wils. Bull.*, 60:6–52, 1948.
157. Tinbergen, N., *The Study of Instinct.* London, Oxford University Press, 1951.
158. Tinbergen, N., *Animal Behavior.* Time-Life, 1966.
159. Tinbergen, N., and Kruyt, W., "Über die Orientierung des Bienen-wolfes III: Die Bevorzugung bestimmter Wegmarken." *Z. vgl. Physiol.*, 25:292–334, 1938.
160. Tinbergen, N., and Kuenen, D. J., "Über die auslösenden und richtungsgebenden Reizsituationen der Sperrbewegung von jungen Drosseln *(Turdus m. merula* L. und Turton, *T. e. ericetorum).*" *Z. Tierpsychol.*, 3:37–60, 1939.
161. Tinbergen, N., *et al.*, "Die Balz des Samtfalters (L: *Eumenis semele)."* *Z. Tierpsychol.*, 5:182–226, 1943.
162. Trumler, E., "Das 'Rossigkeitsgesicht' und ähnliches Ausdrucksver-halten bei Einhufern." *Z. Tierpsychol.*, 16:478–88, 1959.
163. Weih, A. S., "Untersuchung über das Wechselsingen (Anaphonie) und über das angeborene Lautschema einiger Feldheuschrecken." *Z. Tierpsychol.*, 8:1–41, 1951.
164. Whitman, C. O., "Animal Behaviour." *Biol. Lect. Mar. Biol. Lab. Woods Hole*, 285–338, 1898.
165. Wickler, W., "Ei-Attrappen und Maulbrüten bei afrikanischen Zich-liden." *Z. Tierpsychol.*, 19:129–64, 1962.
166. Wickler, W., "Die Evolution von Mustern der Zeichnung und des Verhaltens." *Die Naturwiss.*, 52:335–41, 1965.
167. Wickler, W. "Vergleichende Verhaltensforschung und Phylogenetik," in G. Heberer, *Die Evolution der Organismen,* 3d ed. (Stuttgart, G. Fischer, 1967), 1:420–508.
168. Wilsoncroft, W. E., and Shupe, D. U., "Tail, Paw and Pup Re-trieving in the Rat." *Psychol. Sci.*, 3:494, 1965.
169. Wolfe, J. B., "Effectiveness of Token-Rewards in Chimpanzees." *Comp. Psychol. Monogr.*, 12:1–72, 1936.
170. *Lexikon für Theologie und Kirche.* Freiburg, 1957.

Index

Index

Abstraction, generalizing, 56–58
Accumulated stimulus phenomenon, 35, 67
Acquired behavior, 51–65
Aggressive behavior, 75–76, 120–22, 126, 129–30, 131, 170–71, 191, 197, 198
Agriculture, development of, 156
Animal behavior, 17–76
   acquired behavior, 51–65
   human behavior and, 17–21, 66–76
   innate behavior patterns, 22–29
   innate recognition, 30–40
   instinct and mood, 41–50
Anthropoid apes, 96, 101–2, 108, 109, 153, 156–57, 188, 197
Appeasement behavior, 195
Appeasement gestures, 37, 38, 39, 146, 147
Appetencies, 42–43, 60, 67, 190
Aristippus, 207
Aristotle, 184, 187
Arthropoda, 153
Artificial environment, 93
Artificial organs. *See* Tools, use of
Arts, the, imagination and, 192–95
Association, 61
Atoms (radicals), 23
Australopithecines, 102, 108, 110–11
Authority, subjugation to, 180–83

"Baby face" diagrams, 71–72
Baer, Karl Ernst von, 12

Barter, human, 156–57
Begging movements, 144, 145
Behavior. *See* Animal behavior; Human behavior; and under various types of behavior
Behavioral disorders, 65
Behavioral formulas, 168, 177
Birthrate, limitation of, 172–73
Bisexuality, 100
Bogdanov, A., 218
Bolk, L., 95–96
Bowlby, J., 164
Brain, the human, 102, 105, 109, 140, 163, 169, 170, 186, 188
Brood-tending behavior, 33, 64, 70, 75, 120, 121, 173
Buddhism, 209

Carmichael, L., 26
Cattle breeding, development of, 156
Cell differentiation, 103
Cellular division, 22, 24
Cerebral integration, 69
Cerebral stimulation, 68
   experiments in, 47–49
Chains of command, 138
Chemical anchorage (molecular hypothesis), theory of, 52
Child development, 163–69
Chordata, 153
Christian religion, 18–19, 74, 207, 210
Chromosomes, 23, 24, 51

Chuang-tze, 206
Cicero, 207
Cinema, the, imagination and, 192, 193
Classification of multicellular organisms, 152–54, 160–61
Coelenterata, 153
Collaboration, human, 134–36
Communication, 105, 111
Communication signals, 150–51
Communism, 212–13
Community formulas, 133
Competition, 157
Concept formation, 56–58, 60
Concepts, 194–95
Conditioned reflexes, 53, 60
Conflict behavior, 90
Constitutions, 137
Constructive play, 92
Control formulas, 169
Convolution of Broca, 102
Coordination, 139–40
Coquetry, feminine, signals of, 148–49
Courtship rituals, 37
Crying, 122
Curiosity, 62, 71, 109
  man and, 87–99
Custom, 138–39, 179

Darwin, Charles, 18, 111, 113, 115, 125–26, 129, 147
Defiance, 93, 166–67
Demagogy, 197–98
Demonstration, learning by, 55–56
Deoxyribonucleic acid (DNA molecules), 53
Departure, point of, 9–13, 20
Derision, 126
Development, 23
Dewey, John, 170
Diogenes, 207, 210
Disdain, signs of, 115
Displacement, 49
Displacement laughter, 128
Displacement movements, 60
Distrust, signs of, 116–17

Dollard, J., 170
Domestication, 50, 68, 73, 96, 97, 173
Dücker, G., 57
Dummies (decoys), 32–34, 35, 63, 72, 73
  supernormal, 35, 36, 72, 73, 192

Early Pleistocene period, 19
Eccles, J. C., 52
Echinodermata, 153
Eibl-Eibesfeldt, Irenaeus, 12, 13, 26, 31, 42, 62, 81, 84, 85, 91, 106, 112, 116, 125, 144, 145, 165
Environment, 67, 89, 90, 93, 165
Epicureanism, 209
Equilibrium, 137
Erikson, E. H., 163
Evolution, theory of, 18, 34, 39, 152, 175, 176
Excitation, 41, 43, 44, 60, 67, 70, 128, 129, 143, 149, 151, 191
Experience, 32, 53, 165, 186
  accumulation of, learning by, 51
Experimental play, 92
Experimentation, 165–66
Exploratory behavior, 91, 189–90, 199

Facial expressions, 26, 83–85, 111–19, 122, 130
Facial muscles, multiplication and differentiation of, 111
Fear, 32, 90, 114–15, 189
Fetalization of man, 96
Fight gestures, 37
Fighting behavior, 33
Fighting games, 92
Finger signals, 148
Fixations, 168, 171, 172
Flight games, 92
Frederick II, 68
Free will, 79, 86
Freedom, 198
  imprinting and, 162–74
  loss of, 182

Freud, Sigmund, 67, 70, 167, 168, 170
Friendship signal, 120–31
Fromme, A., 26
Frustration, 170–71
Frustration and Aggression (Dollard et al.), 169–70

Ganglion cells, 60, 102, 108
Gehlen, A., 93, 95, 98, 187, 194
Genome, 26
Germ cells, 22–23, 100, 154
Gestalt perception, 12
Gestures, 37, 38, 39, 85, 142–51
Goethe, Johann Wolfgang von, 206, 207, 212
Goodall, Jane, 36, 58, 59, 84, 144
Gossen, Herman, 67
Government, 158, 195, 212
Graphic arts, imagination and, 193
Greeting, forms of, 144–45
movements of, 124
Grohmann, J., 26
Grooming behavior, 42. *See also* Skin-tending motions
Guidance formulas, 138, 140

Habits, 60, 190
Hall, Stanley, 170
Hand, the prehensile, 101, 106, 109, 163, 165
Hand movements, 143, 147–48
Handbuch der Biologie (Eibl-Eibesfeldt), 125
Handicrafts, development of, 104
Happiness, quest for, 199–214
Head-shaking signals, 147
Herd instinct, 178
Hereditary coordination, 30, 32, 36, 41, 42, 46, 48, 53, 60, 62, 63, 70, 82, 85, 89
Hereditary formulas, 23–29, 65, 69, 154, 159, 160, 162, 176, 177, 190
Heredity, 19, 20, 21, 23, 25, 79, 92
Mendelian laws of, 25
Hering, E., 53
Hess, E. H., 61, 63, 64, 168

Hidden Persuaders, The (Packard), 183
Hölderlin, Friedrich, 207
Holst, E. von, 28, 29, 44, 47, 48, 49, 69, 74
Horace, 207
Hormones, operation of, 45
Human behavior, 79–214
animal behavior and, 17–21, 66–76
facial expressions, 111–19
gestures, 142–51
happiness, quest for, 199–214
imagination and, 186–98
imprinting and freedom, 162–74
inquisitive behavior and, 87–99, 109
multicellular organism and, 152–61
order and, 132–41
self-explanation, 79–86
smiling and laughter, 120–31
society and, 175–81
tools, use of, 100–9
Humani generis (papal encyclical), 19
Hunting games, 92

Ideas, 186, 189, 190, 194
Identification disorders, 167
Imagination, 109
man and, 186–98
Imitative behavior, 93, 178–79
learning by, 52, 55
Immobility, 114
Impatience, sign for, 149
Impressive behavior, 179–80, 182–83, 191
Imprinting, 54, 63–65, 67, 69, 193
freedom and, 162–74
Imprisonment, 82–83
Impulsion mechanisms, innate, 69
Inhibitory mechanism, 38
Initiative, 168
Innate behavior patterns, 51, 54, 60, 65, 176
Innate recognition, 30–40, 134

Innate releasing mechanism (IRM), 29, 30, 31, 32, 34, 41, 50, 95, 143
Inquisitive behavior, 87–99, 109. *See also* Curiosity
Instinctive behavior, 26–29, 41–50, 62, 63, 68, 73–74, 88, 89, 95, 139
Instincts, 171, 178, 182, 188–89, 191, 197, 198
parliament of, 43, 44, 69, 188
Intelligence, 93, 101, 109, 156, 188
Intelligent behavior, 56, 58–59
Intent, movements of, 42, 112–13, 114, 115, 143–44
Interest, signs of, 113–14, 115
Invention, 187

Kant, Immanuel, 67, 196
Keeping in order, 136, 139
Key stimulus, 30, 32–38, 41, 50, 54, 57, 70, 71, 79, 95, 121, 134
Koehler, O., 35, 58
Koran, the, 211
Kortlandt, A., 108
Kruijt, J. P., 31

Labor, division of, 133, 140, 152, 153, 156
Lamarck, Jean de, 115
Lamarckians, 18
Lao-tse, 207, 209
Laughter and laughing, 125, 126–29
Leadership, 121
Leakey, L. S. D., 110
Learning, 51–65, 67, 69, 89
aptitude for, 27
processes of, 20
Legislation, 138
Lehrmann, D. S., 45
Linnaeus, Carolus, 152
Literature, imagination and, 191–92, 193
Livelihood, forms of, 155–56
Lorenz, Konrad, 20, 36, 37, 41, 42, 43, 48, 49, 50, 61, 63, 68, 71–72, 73, 75, 89, 92, 95, 96–97, 98, 108–9, 113, 120, 124–25, 126, 168, 197, 203

Man. *See* Human behavior
Maturation, delayed, 61
Mechanisms, 25, 26–27, 29, 33, 38, 51, 66, 69, 70, 86, 121
Memory, 52–54, 105, 186, 187
Memory traces (engrams), 52
Mendelian laws of heredity, 25
Mental disorders, 170
Metazoa, 153, 154
Mistrust, basic, 164
Mobility, personal, 166
Mockery, 126
Mollusca, 153
Money, invention of, 157
Mood, 42, 44, 67
transmission of, 71, 177–78
Moral concepts, 73, 74, 171, 172, 193
Morris, Desmond, 9, 94
Motivation for learning, 61–62
Motor control, innate structures of, 26
Movements, 23, 25, 29, 30, 35, 38, 42, 60, 61, 70, 142
facial, 111–19
of intent, 42, 112–13, 114, 115, 143–44
Multicellular organisms, 100, 103
man and, 152–61
Music, imagination and, 193
Mutations, 18, 159–60

National exultation, imagination and, 197–98
Natural-selection process, 18, 34, 37, 50, 97, 115, 142, 157
Neoteny, 96–97
Nerve cells, 24, 29, 66
Nervous system, central, 154, 160, 186
Neuroses, 171
Nietzsche, F. W., 98, 200, 206
Novelty, 88, 90, 93

Occupations, human, development of, 104, 154–58
Oedipal period, 167
Olduvai Gorge, Tanzania, 110

On Aggression (Lorenz), 75, 120
Order, keeping in, 136, 139
  men and, 132–41
Organizations, productive, 158–59,
  181
Organs, 100–1, 102
  artificial. *See* Tools, use of
Orientation, 81

Packard, Vance, 183
Painting, imagination and, 192–93
Parliament of instincts, 43, 44, 69,
  188
Pavlov, Ivan P., 28, 60
Permissiveness, 170
Picasso, Pablo, 193
Plans, 190
Plants, 18, 22, 23, 106, 153, 175
Plastic arts, imagination and, 193
Play behavior, 62, 89–90, 91–93, 94–
  98, 187, 189–90
Pleasure, procurement of, 157–58,
  165
Plenge, J., 218
Ploog, D. W., 43
Porifera, 153
Power, balance of, 132–33
Power systems, 180–83
Primitive man, 102–3, 108, 110–11,
  112, 156, 164, 215
Priorities, 92
Productive systems, 154–61
Progesterone, 45
Property, problem of, 104
Protection, 90–91, 105–6, 198
Protozoa, 153, 154
Psychoanalysis, 67, 168, 169

Reafference, 69
Reason, 189
Recognition, innate, 30–40, 134
Reflexes, 28–29, 31, 53, 60, 69, 164
Regulatory cycles, 69
Relaxation, zone of, 98
Releasers, 34–38, 71–73

Religion, 74, 139, 172
  evolution and, 18–19
  imagination and, 195–96
Rensch, B., 57, 60
Ritualization, 38–39, 113, 116, 118,
  142, 146, 149–50
Roman Catholic Church, 18–19

Saint-Paul, U. von, 47, 48
Sales technique, 183–84
Salutation gestures, 144–45
Scenting, 82
Schiller, J. von, 94
Sculpture, imagination and, 192–93
Seitz, A., 35
Selective stimuli, 31
Self-exploration, 79–86
Self-expression, 170
Seneca, 207
Sensations, 71
Sexual behavior, 64, 69–70, 74–75,
  167, 168, 173–74
Sexual maturity, 96, 151
Sexual organs, 101
Sign language, soundless, 111
Signal stimuli, 34, 38, 39
Skin-tending motions, 36, 124
Smiles and smiling, 120–31
Social instincts, 73
Social order, 133
Society, human, man and, 175–81
Spatial coordination, 139–40
Spatial order, 136
Spatiotemporal order, 161
Spencer, Herbert, 128
Spitz, R. A., 43, 164
State, the, 137
Stimuli, 30–38, 40, 41, 66
  key, 30, 32–38, 41, 50, 54, 57, 70,
    71, 79, 95, 121, 134
  selective, 31
  signal, 34, 38, 39
  unselective, 31–32
Stimulus thresholds, 67
  lowering and raising of, 44–46,
    48, 60
Stoics, 207

Subjugation, 180–83
Submission gestures, 145, 146
Superindividuality, 159
Supernormal dummies, 35, 36, 72, 73, 192
Surrogates (substitutes), 42, 92
Symbiosis, 37
Symbolic gestures, 146

Temporal order, 140
Theater, the, imagination and, 192, 193
Thucydides, 211
Time sense, human, 12
Tinbergen, N., 20, 34–35, 44, 46, 49
Tools, use of, 48, 58–59, 97, 100–9
Transformation, 49
Trial and error, learning by, 51, 54
Trust, basic, 163–65, 168
Turgor, 23

Understanding. *See* Intelligence
Unicellular organisms, 18, 20, 22, 24, 28, 52, 100, 153
Universal order, 137
Unselective stimuli, 31–32
Usage, order of, 138–39, 179

Value judgments, development of, 167–68
Variety, 88
Vitalists, 18

Whitman, C. O., 50
Whole and Part in the Animal and Human Community (Lorenz), 95
Will, human, 168, 171, 177
Wolfe, J. B., 156

Zagarus, A., 35